Castleton C

Trevor D. Ford

With Photographs by Paul Deakin

Landmark Publishing

Contents

Foreword

More than 60 years ago, about 1941, as a schoolboy, I started guiding visitors round the Speedwell Mine. I pushed the boat along the underground canal and explained the history of the late 18th-century mining venture to the mid-20th-century tourists. During those war years of the 1940s, Dick Howes, Bob Woolhouse, Dave Sampson and others were allowed to explore beyond the Bottomless Pit and I joined them whenever possible. Dick Howes commenced a survey and I held the other end of the tape. It all led to my love of the Castleton caves, which has persisted to the present day. During my student days in 1949 I was one of the helpers with the Cave Diving Group in Peak Cavern and managed to get through the Mucky Ducks in a diving suit, though without breathing apparatus, so I was among the first party to hike up the Upper Gallery and reach the Surprise View. Another group siphoned water out of the Mucky Ducks and reached the Surprise View a week later. Subsequently a few of my own discoveries spurred others into further explorations, such as Pilkington's Cavern. Regrettably, age and infirmity have prevented my partaking in the recent exciting discoveries such as the White River Series, Leviathan and Titan, but I have taken much pleasure in seeing such places through others' eyes.

There are four tourist caves at Castleton, each showing different features and offering a story of their own in the following chapters. There are also the "wild" caves which have not been developed for public visiting and which have their own story to tell. Cavers, both novices and experts, spend many happy hours in them, and exploration continues.

Since World War II the conservation of natural features has become an important issue and the Castleton cave systems are now part of a Site of Special Scientific Interest administered by Natural England (formerly the Nature Conservancy, later English Nature). The Castleton area is much used for school and university teaching purposes as well as being a "honeypot" for tourists. It lies within the Peak District National Park and presents an important collection of geological, geomorphological and speleological features, perhaps worthy of UNESCO Geopark status.

I have assembled this book in such a way as to let readers, whether cavers or the general public, have an insight into the way cave explorers operate and what they have discovered. It has given me the chance to assemble a description of the complex cave systems and to deduce an outline of how the caves may have evolved over millions of years. It will be obvious that there are gaps in our knowledge, though hopefully future exploration may fill some of them, so this book should perhaps be regarded as a summary of the state of play in 2008.

Acknowledgements

I wish to thank several of my past research students, notably John Beck, Noel Christopher, Jim Rieuwerts and Richard Shaw, for their comments and permission to use some of their thesis diagrams herein. Dave Nixon, Tony Marsden, John Cordingley, Paul Chandler, Chris Heathcote and John Gunn have allowed me to use some of their reports and diagrams. Dave Nixon and Tony Waltham have read parts of the text and supplied useful comments. Lisa Barber has kindly redrawn some of the diagrams. Paul Deakin, F.R.P.S. (P.D.), John Cordingley (J.N.C.), Richard Shaw (R.P.S.), Tony Waltham (A.C.W.) and Tony Marsden (A.M.) have kindly supplied photographs (credited with their initials after the captions). A few photos are by unknown photographers. The owners of the tourist caves are thanked for allowing me access.

1 THE CASTLETON KARST

Karst is a collective term for limestone landscapes, caves and other features, derived from the Kras region of Croatia in the former Yugoslavia. Castleton lies at the northern tip of the Peak District limestone massif, commonly known as the White Peak in contradistinction from the Dark Peak of the Millstone Grit country to the north. Thus the White Peak is karst country, though much less rugged than in Croatia and with its own association of karst features.

The limestones of the White Peak were deposited in the tropical seas of mid-Carboniferous times, roughly 330 to 300 million years ago, when Britain lay near the Equator. Most of the limestones were formed in shallow lagoons comparable with those found in Pacific atolls today; surrounded by marginal reefs (mud-mounds, bioherms or build-ups in geological literature). The Derbyshire reefs differ from modern reefs in their sparsity of corals: other organisms built the reefs, particularly mats of marine algae (microscopic plants), crinoids, bryozoans and a great variety of shells. Wave action broke their remains down to lime sand or lime mud deposited on the floor of the lagoon. Thus Castleton has lagoonal limestones forming the plateau to the south, and a rim of reefs extending from Pindale in the east, across Cavedale, Peak Cavern Gorge and the Winnats Pass, Treak Cliff, Windy Knoll, Peakshill and on to Perryfoot. The reef-belt is characterized by masses of irregular mound-shaped structures of fine-grained reef limestone, with coarse-grained back reef limestones fringing the lagoon and representing wave-washed detritus, and with steep outer fore-reef slopes also composed of wave-washed debris forming slopes descending into the deeper water of a basin to the north.

The earliest limestones were laid down on a basement of slaty rocks of Ordovician age of which little is known. The basement is nowhere exposed but was penetrated in a borehole 1,600m deep at Eyam: it is probably at a comparable depth below Castleton and was covered by limestones in early Carboniferous times. This yielded a thick sequence of limestone beds available for cave development both in the exposed White Peak and in the deeper beds far below any visible today. There were brief breaks in sedimentation which gave rise to partings between the limestone beds known as bedding planes, sometimes occupied with a few centimetres of shale or of volcanic ash – the latter are known as wayboards. Other less frequent breaks were due to outpourings of basaltic lava onto the floor of the lagoon. Bedding planes, wayboards and lavas were later to be significant in cave initiation.

Movements of the Earth's crust at the end of the limestone era caused the limestone mass to be raised above sea level, so that the topmost limestone beds were eroded off and boulders slid or rolled down the submarine slope to yield a Boulder Bed along the foot of the outer reef slope. The higher parts of Castleton's karst limestone massif were exposed to erosion above sea level, resulting in ancient caves and other palaeokarstic features. The same movements caused stresses which initiated fissures in the limestone.

There were several small volcanoes in the White Peak's lagoon and intermittent eruptions resulted in basaltic lava flows, locally known as toadstones, and clay wayboards, well known to the Derbyshire lead miners as poor in the lead ores they sought. At Castleton the only visible toadstones are the Cavedale Lava and the so-called Speedwell vent; the former outcrops in Cavedale and extends beneath some of the adjacent limestones as a sheet of toadstone some 20m thick, though it dies out to the north-west. The Speedwell vent is a fragmented basaltic rock known as "agglomerate", visible over a few hundred square metres at the foot of the fore-reef slope of Cowlow, between Peak and Speedwell Caverns. It is of uncertain origin and may either mark the site of an underwater volcano at the foot of the outer reef slope or where lava tumbled down that slope from the Cavedale lava through a gap in the reef-belt. Explosive eruptions yielded showers of volcanic ash or tuff, forming the clay wayboards between limestone beds. These may be more common than their brief outcrops suggest but examples are limited: wayboards are visible underground in Nettle Pot, JH Mine, Titan and in various localities in

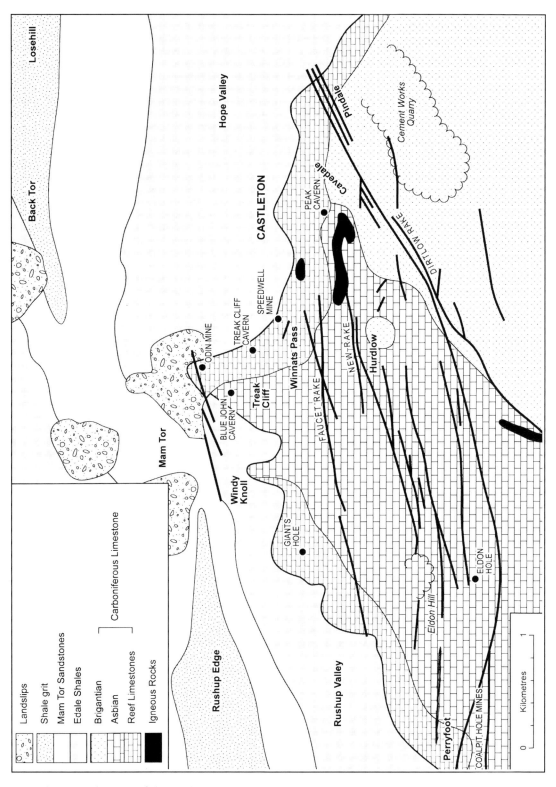

An outline geological map of the Castleton area.

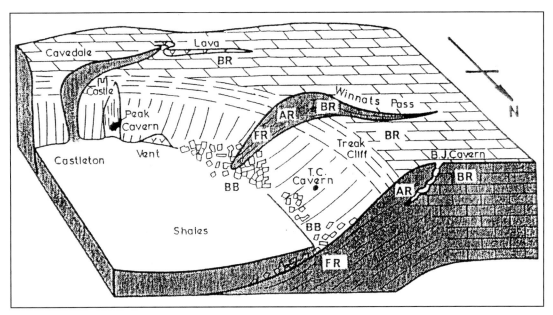

Diagram of part of the Castleton reef belt with the later Cavedale and Winnats Pass (AR = algal reefs; BR = back reef; FR = fore-reef; BB = boulder bed).

the further reaches of Peak and Speedwell Caverns.

Extensional stresses in the Earth's crust oriented roughly NNE–SSW opened fractures in the limestone mass at the end of limestone sedimentation. Many of the fractures show horizontal slickensides (grooved or polished surfaces where rock masses have moved past each other during faulting) on their walls indicating that they were wrench faults: where it can be determined they show dextral lateral movement. The slickensides mostly date from late Carboniferous times, when the fractures were re-opened and filled with minerals to form the veins sought by lead miners.

A drastic change of geography at the end of the limestone period resulted in massive deltas building out from rivers draining both the ancestral Scottish Highlands and from as far away as Greenland (the Atlantic Ocean had not then been opened and

Greenland was close to Scotland). The deltas deposited vast sheets of sandy and muddy sediments, now represented by the sandstones and shales which make up the Millstone Grit of the Pennines. In turn these were covered by the delta-swamp sediments of the Coal Measures, now restricted to the coalfields on either flank of the Pennines, but once stretching right across from Lancashire to Yorkshire and Derbyshire. Together these strata buried the limestone to a depth of around two kilometres by the end of the Carboniferous period, around 290 million years ago.

Whilst buried beneath the Millstone Grit and Coal Measures, movements of the Earth's crust in the latest Carboniferous caused up-arching of the region by east–west compression to form the beginnings of the Pennine Anticline. The complementary extensional stress field resulted in renewed opening of the earlier fractures

and the formation of others.

An influx of mineralizing fluids derived from adjacent sedimentary basins filled the fractures with a suite of hydrothermal minerals to yield the vein system. The larger mineral veins are known as rakes and generally have a WSW–ENE trend: they include Faucet, New and Dirtlow Rakes. Subsidiary veins or scrins have either W–E or WNW–ESE trends. The minerals include galena, sphalerite, fluorite, baryte and calcite, which crystallized from fluids at temperatures of around 80 to 120°C. Old lead mine shafts along the veins are marked with lines of waste heaps and occasional open-cuts. Minerals deposited along bedding planes yielded veins known as flats. Ancient caves formed in a mid-Carboniferous palaeokarst phase were filled or lined with minerals and are known today as pipe veins. The pipe veins include the caverns lined with Blue John fluorite in Treak Cliff. Other

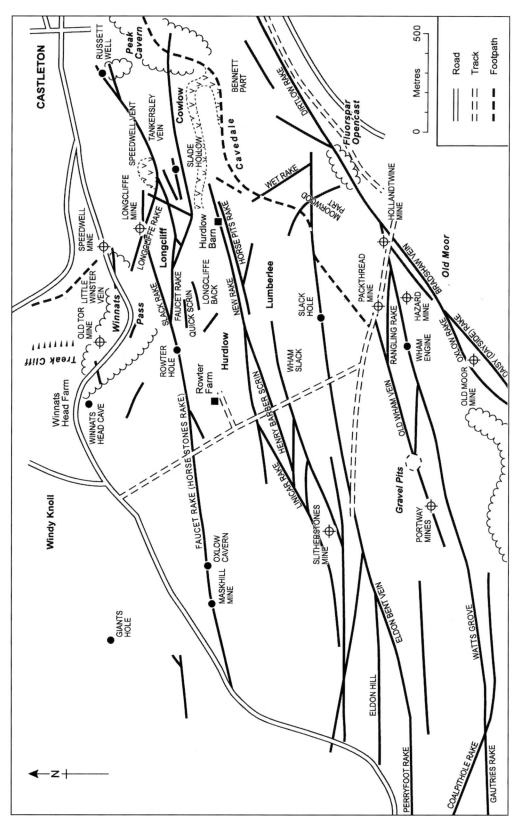

Sketch map of the mineral veins.

Winnats Pass

pipes tend to lie along certain bedding planes or wayboards within the limestone massif and so may have no outcrop. Incomplete mineral fills in both fissure veins and pipes left cavities between the minerals, commonly known as vugs, which, again, were later incorporated in the early development of caves.

From the end of the Carboniferous period, the next 290 million years of geological time are not represented by any strata in the area around Castleton and our knowledge of the geological history of the Peak District has to be inferred by projection from surrounding regions. It is uncertain what thickness of strata of Triassic, Jurassic and Cretaceous age once lay above the Peak District, but whatever was laid down has been eroded off, so that we have to jump to somewhere around 5 to 10 million years ago, when further earth movements continued the uplift of the Pennine anticline. The uplift allowed erosion to strip off any remaining

cover of Millstone Grit and Coal Measures, gradually uncovering the underlying limestone. By Pliocene times, say 3 to 5 million years ago, continental drift had taken Britain to near its present latitude, 50 degrees north of the Equator, and normal temperate weathering processes were available to erode the forerunner of today's karst landscape.

In the Quaternary era, from 1.8 million years ago to the present, the glaciers of the Pleistocene Ice Age intermittently covered much of Britain but their effects were limited to episodes of 20,000 to 100,000 years or so. The glacial episodes were separated by warm interglacial climatic phases lasting for similar time spans and sometimes warmer than at present. The last 13,000 years is the Holocene Period, which saw a return to normal temperate processes in today's cool to warm climatic conditions. Some of the cold episodes saw the plateau at least frozen if not covered by ice sheets. In effect, when

glaciers did not reach the White Peak, periglacial conditions pervaded the area and the landscape was comparable with today's frozen tundra of Alaska and Siberia, probably with permafrost (frozen ground) in the limestone. It is during the alternation of warm, cold and not-so-cold periods that the landscape acquired the present-day features seen today as the limestone plateau of the White Peak, with its underground drainage systems and caves. The freeze and thaw alternation also led to the formation of a solifluction sheet of sandy material (loose sediment which has sludged downhill by freeze and thaw processes) blanketing the southern slopes of Rushup Edge and washing into the swallets (a local term for streams disappearing underground, also known as sinkholes or swallow holes).

Vein cavities were only recognized as a distinctive feature of Castleton's karst during the 1980s. They are generally nearly vertical caverns oriented along mineral veins and developed by phreatic solution (dissolution of limestone below the water table) over a long period. As the water table fell they were partly drained. The most accessible example is the Bottomless Pit in Speedwell Cavern. Small examples partly filled with sediment may be seen in the preserved north-west face of the fluorspar opencast on Dirtlow Rake.

Dolines are solution hollows characteristic of many karst areas overseas: they are funnel-shaped hollows usually sited on intersections of joints and rainwater is channelled down them to caves beneath. Dolines are not common in the Peak District but Castleton has a scatter. Enclosed hollows perhaps 50 to 100m in diameter and 10 to 20m deep occur in the fields southeast of Eldon quarry, near Hazard Mine and on New Rake south of Rowter Farm. Their position suggests that there are collapsed caverns beneath but the only one tested by excavation is Slack Hole near the top of Cavedale, where a shaft dug by cavers found only a mass of boulders and no cave was reached.

Under tundra conditions fine-grained sediment is lifted from the bare ground of the Millstone Grit country by the wind and redeposited on the limestone as a silty clay known as loess. Patches of loess subsoil, commonly a metre or so thick, lie beneath the modern soil and turf over much of the Castleton area. Under subsequent erosional conditions, ochreous silt and mud derived from the loess was washed down into the caves, forming yellowish mud completely filling cave passages in places.

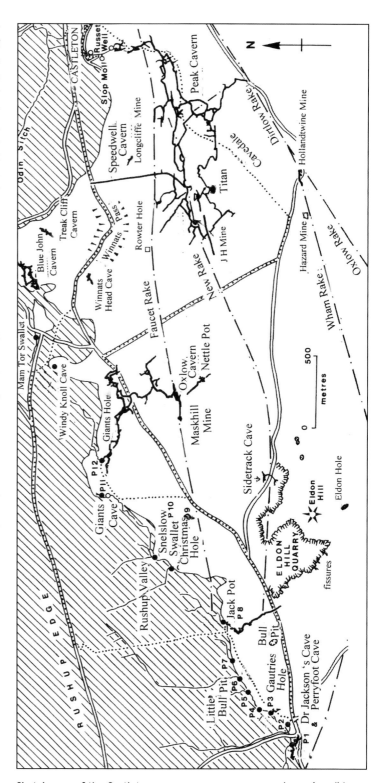

Sketch map of the Castleton caves - cave passages are shown in solid black.

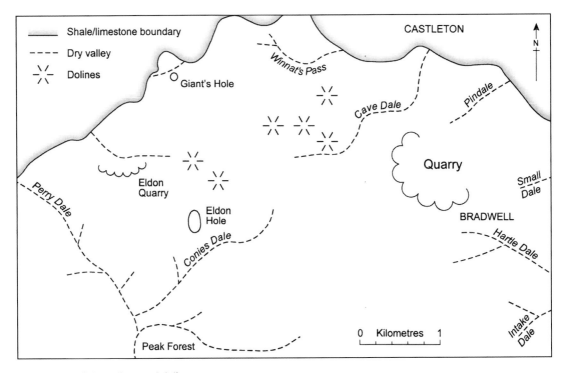

Sketch map of dry valleys and dolines.

Dry valleys (without streams) were formed by run-off during the frozen ground phases of periglacial periods and a network diversifies the plateau with such features including Cavedale, Pindale, Conies Dale, Perry Dale and the Winnats Pass (the last-named has a long and more complex history having been initiated as a gap in the reef-belt in Carboniferous times). Rainfall during the warmer periods ran off as cave streams, augmented in colder periods with meltwater from thick snow cover, contributing to the enlargement of the cave systems both by dissolving limestone and by abrading it with inwashed sand.

Caves often contain speleothems such as stalactites, stalagmites and other calcite formations caused by percolating rainwater losing carbon dioxide to the cave atmosphere and causing calcium carbonate to be deposited. Apart from their aesthetic appeal, the stalactite formations can yield dates by analyzing their contained traces of uranium and its daughter radioactive products. Many Castleton caves have been sampled for datable speleothems and the dates provide a framework for constructing an outline of a sequence of developmental stages (see the chapter on speleogenesis), though future research would be aided by many more determinations.

This book is concerned with the cave systems and these are described in the following chapters, concluding with a proposed sequence of developmental events in the chapter on speleogenesis. Dating events, both on the surface and underground, has many problems. To some extent phases of cave evolution can be related to the development of surface features, but there are uncertainties in our story which await future research.

Many caves elsewhere have their entrances filled with deposits containing relics of occupation by wild animals or occasionally by early man. There are only a few such bone caves around Castleton, but the best known is Windy Knoll Cave, which yielded thousands of bones of late Pleistocene mammals. A shelter in Cavedale had both post-glacial mammal bones and a few traces of Iron Age man. A Bronze Age burial site was found in a sepulchral cave above Treak Cliff Cavern. None of the bone caves has been investigated by modern archaeological methods so their contribution to our knowledge of cave evolution is limited.

Open cave mouths were often occupied by animals or occasionally occupied by early man, though there would be little attempt to explore beyond the limits of daylight. However, little archaeological evidence has been found in the Castleton area, except for Windy Knoll Cave. Peak Cavern's large entrance would almost certainly attract Stone Age man as a habitation site but no archaeological investigation is known to have taken place. A few finds of bones suggest that wild animals used the cavern as a den. There are various legends of mediaeval explorations, some said to have found underground worlds of green fields! Cave exploration in historical times was largely limited to lead miners seeking ores via caves; indeed many of the caves known today were found by the miners. Caves were long regarded as habitations of the Devil himself and the occasional tourists overcame their superstitions to see such places as the Devil's Arse. In the 18th and 19th centuries artists were attracted by the entrance to Peak Cavern and their engravings portray the cave and gorge with varying degrees of accuracy or exaggeration.

Cave excavation for evidence of prehistoric man and contemporary animals was stimulated by the publication of Charles Darwin's *Origin of Species* in 1859, but little in the way of deeper exploration took place until the end of the 19th century and early 20th century. Cave exploration as we know it today began then, though some of the accounts are highly exaggerated and need careful interpretation. Cave explorers were usually known as potholers and wore old clothes which gave minimal protection against the cold, wet and muddy conditions. Lighting was mostly by candles, sometimes stuck to their hats by lumps of clay. Miners' helmets with brackets to carry acetylene lamps came into use by World War I, but electric cap lamps with rechargeable batteries on the belt as used in coal mines were not common amongst cavers until after World War II. In these conditions, primitive in modern eyes, the explorers penetrated many of the cave systems known today.

Among the obstacles encountered by the early explorers were deep water, vertical drops and passages blocked with sediments or rock falls. The first could require swimming but rafts or collapsible boats were sometimes carried in. Pre-1950 explorations of the Speedwell Mine's Far Canal used a coffin-like boat kept afloat by petrol cans tied on the outside! The introduction of neoprene wetsuits as used by sea divers and surfers made wet caving much more comfortable, generally without the need for boats. Divers' drysuits are sometimes used today.

Vertical drops are known to cavers as pitches: up to the 1950s they were tackled with ropes or rope ladders made of sisal rope and wooden rungs, heavy and clumsy to handle and the ropes were liable to rot in the damp conditions. One rope ladder in use in an early exploration of Peak Cavern's Surprise View pitch broke on both sides, depositing the climber on the people below! Early explorations of Eldon Hole were made by lowering men on a single rope. In the early 20th century this technique was improved with a complicated arrangement of pulleys.

After World War II lightweight "electron" ladders appeared; with steel wire sides and aluminium alloy rungs, they were much more durable and easier to handle and transport. In the last 20 years or so single rope technique (SRT) has been adapted from mountaineering usage. Abseiling down and prusiking up a single synthetic rope has become commonplace, though requiring training and experience. Climbing up caves rising vertically (usually known as avens from the French term) above the access passage was largely regarded as impossible by early explorers, though ordi-

Climbing Cliff Cavern

nary wooden ladders were occasionally carried in. The advent of battery-powered masonry drills in the 1970s meant that bolting upwards became possible, and many high avens were explored from the bottom upwards. The explorer dangled from a Rawlbolt whilst drilling another hole a little higher and so moved upwards a bit at a time. The massive Titan chamber, over 140 metres high, was climbed using this method.

All too often cave passages end at sumps (formerly called siphons), where the onward route is completely submerged. The answer was cave-diving: started in the Mendip Hills of Somerset in the 1930s using clumsy lead-weighted canvas suits, a post World War II improvement was the use of "frogman" suits, particularly in Peak Cavern. The rubberized canvas diving suits were still cumbersome, and the oxygen-breathing apparatuses were limited to 10m depth as oxygen is toxic at greater depths. Several major discoveries were made in the 1940s and 1950s, notably the Far Peak stream caves. Diving technology has advanced since then and today's divers use drysuits, insulated from the cold, occasionally with built-in heating. Breathing oxygen–helium or oxygen–nitrogen mixtures permits much greater depths to be explored, but has the problem of needing long decompression halts on the return. Underwater lighting has developed from a hand-held battery-operated Aflo (strictly Aflolaun – apparatus for laying out line and underwater navigation) to powerful helmet-mounted flashlights. Even with present-day breathing apparatus and lighting technology, a frequent problem with cave-diving is visibility: the water is often muddy and the diver himself stirs up even more mud, so that guide lines have to be laid for the diver to feel his way back.

Many cave passages have been blocked with sediments washed in by ancient streams or by rocks falling from higher passages. Blockages are often cemented by flowstone deposits. Digging may allow explorers to get past the blockage, but it can be a hit-or-miss affair and may take years before it pays dividends. There is little doubt that future discoveries will be made mostly by persistent digging.

All cave exploration should be followed by surveying to make as accurate as possible a record of the cave. Most cave surveys are by compass and tape and taking readings in dark, wet and cramped spaces can lead to errors compared with surface surveying techniques. Wherever practical, closed loops reduce the errors. Further improvements may be attained by using radio-location. A magnetized coil is laid out in the cave and a search coil is moved around on the surface to find a point directly above the site in the cave. Successive searches over a series of locations in a cave can tie the underground layout to the surface and so produce a more accurate survey.

Cave exploration falls into three categories. Sporting cavers enjoy the challenge of getting to the bottom of known caves and this is usually a matter for local caving clubs with around 30 to 100 members. More dedicated sporting cavers go in for the practical pursuits of surveying to provide us with cave plans and photographs for illustrating reports. Finally, there are scientific cavers or speleologists who study the features of the cave to work out its evolution: they look at hydrology and drainage, study the biology of animals found underground or search for bones as evidence of previous occupation by man or animals. Some sporting cavers are stimulated into becoming cave scientists.

Newcomers to caving are advised to join one of the local caving clubs for guidance on clothing, equipment and techniques: a list can be obtained from Peak Park Information centres or from the Derbyshire Caving Association, c/o 3 Greenway, Hulland Ward, Ashbourne, Derbyhire, DE6 3FE (www.thedca.org.uk).

The *British Caving Association* (http://british-caving.org.uk) is an umbrella organization looking after matters of national interest such as access, training, insurance and overseas expeditions. The *British Cave Research Association* (http://bcra.org.uk) encourages education, research and conservation, publishes a journal (*Cave and Karst Science*), and maintains a library and archives. Regional caving councils, such as the *Derbyshire Caving Association* (www.thedca.org.uk), oversee local matters such as club accreditation, training, planning and development. Some caves are registered as Sites of Special Scientific Interest by *Natural England* (successor to the Nature Conservancy), which has a statutory responsibility for conservation. Much of the Castleton cave system has been designated a Site of Special Scientific Interest (SSSI).

The ramifications of Peak Cavern make it the longest cave system in the Peak District, and one of the longest in Britain. With its several underground links to Speedwell Cavern, if the many passages and caverns in the latter are included, some 16km of passages are now known in the combined Peak–Speedwell cave system. Of these, the first kilometre of Peak Cavern has been a tourist show cave for centuries.

The vast entrance archway is at the head of a short blind gorge beneath the ruins of Peveril Castle. The entrance arch is 35m wide and 15m high and behind it the Vestibule stretches back more than 100m. The Peakshole stream rises from the Resurgence just outside the entrance, and cave-divers have reached the isolated Schoolroom Rift a few metres in, and have also dived through to the Swine Hole off the Vestibule. The Resurgence stream comes through impenetrable passages from Halfway House, some 300m to the south. Together with the discharge from Russet Well the Peakshole Water flows north out of the gorge and then turns eastwards along the floor of Hope Valley to join the River Noe near Hope: in turn the Noe forms a major tributary of the River Derwent at Bamford.

With the largest cave entrance in Britain, it is not surprising that Peak Cavern attracted attention in early times. The terraces cut into the sloping bank of sediments in the Vestibule have been used for at least four centuries as a rope walk. Rope was made by hand for many purposes including haulage in the local lead mines. Some of the rope workers lived in hovels against the west wall, where soot from their smoky fires still covers parts of the roof. Rope was made on wooden frames whilst twine was stretched from high poles. It is highly likely that long before being adapted for rope-making, the great bank of sediments would have been used as a habitation site in prehistoric times, but no archaeological investigation is known to have taken place. Occasional bones of wild animals such as boar have been found. A normally dry channel along the east wall carries a substantial stream from Lumbago Walk under flood conditions.

There are scattered references to what was then known as the *Devil's Arse* in literature dating back to the 12th century and this name has been revived recently. The poet Thomas Hobbes described it in Latin verse in the 17th century. However, few accounts record any reliable details until the late 18th century, when artistic engravings gave a reasonable idea of the present tourist cave. The name Devil's Arse has been attributed to the obscene noises made when air trapped by floods bubbles out, though in olden days any cave was regarded as a residence of the Devil. Drawings by the artist Sir Francis Chantrey appeared in several books in the 19th century.

Along the roof of the west side of the Vestibule there are high chimney-like chambers decorated with massive tufa stalactites; high above the tourist path these lie on a strong north–south joint but no passages leading off have been found. Low on the opposite side of the Vestibule a tunnel is the Swine Hole, a phreatic tube leading to flooded passages whence cave-divers have been able to emerge at the Resurgence in the gorge outside. Swine Hole takes part

Rope Walks in Peak Cavern (P.D)

Peak Cavern – an early engraving by I. Stockdale, Piccadilly, London, dated 1794.

of the flood water when Lumbago Walk is flooded. Above and to the right of the Swine Hole a sloping passage extends upwards towards Cavedale.

At the inner end of the Vestibule, the visitors' route slopes down into Lumbago Walk, which requires stooping to reach the River Styx. Here early tourists were ferried across a pool lying in a low boat pushed by the guides wading behind. As a young princess, Queen Victoria was taken through this and, as a result of her comments, a bypass passage was subsequently blasted out and forms today's route into the Great Cave. Both Lumbago Walk and the Styx bypass are liable to flooding with some of the water rising from an impenetrable sump on the right, which also emits the strange gurgling noises.

The Great Cave is one of the largest interior caverns in Britain at some 40m diameter and 20m high, lying beneath the amphitheatre of Cavedale. The roof shows phreatic solution features indicating an origin when the cave was under water. On the left (east) slope a patch of sand may conceal a branch passage. High in the roof on the right (west) a narrow chimney once connected to a hole in Cavedale. It was first explored by Puttrell early in the 20th century, and another caver descending on a single rope in the 1950s appeared in front of a guide and party of visitors. The caver was deaf and could not hear the guide's protests. Later the hole was fitted with a grille for safety. Long ago, animals occasionally fell down this and their bones have been found on the sediment slope. At the top of the right-hand slope of the Great Cave a short passage leads to the Orchestra some 12m above the tourist path in Roger Rain's House. Musicians were once hired to entertain important visitors, and occasional Christmas concerts are still held.

Keeping to the main route the visitor soon reaches Roger Rain's House where a heavy shower of drips falls from the roof, directly below where a small stream sinks close to the line of a thin mineral vein off Faucet Rake which crosses the floor of Cavedale.

Soon after Roger Rain's House the present-day tourist route ends at Pluto's Dining Room, with a short branch passage to the right (west) which was probably an inlet streamway but is

Peak Cavern – engraving of the Ropewalks (drawn by F. Chantrey for E. Rhodes "Peak Scenery", 1822).

now blocked with rocks after about 40m. On the opposite side of Pluto's Dining Room a concealed hole rises upwards for 3m and a passage crosses back above the roof towards the Five Arches; 50m long, it is now known as the Devil's Cellar. The now ruined Devil's Staircase goes steeply downwards beyond the Dining Room. It leads to an impressive stream cave with the Five Arches separating high fissures above the streamway and thence to the vast chamber known as Victoria Aven. One of the fissures links to a small cave in Cavedale. Drips from a trickle down one fissure have deeply grooved the wall. The tourist route once included these de-

Castleton Caves

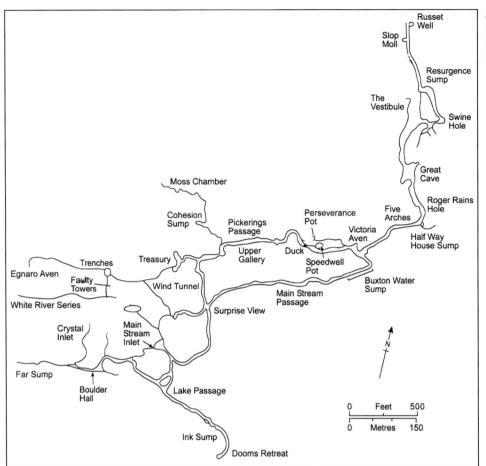

An outline plan of Peak Cavern.

- Russet Well
- Slop Moll
- Resurgence Sump
- The Vestibule
- Swine Hole
- Great Cave
- Roger Rains Hole
- Moss Chamber
- Cohesion Sump
- Pickerings Passage
- Perseverance Pot
- Five Arches
- Treasury
- Upper Gallery
- Duck
- Victoria Aven
- Half Way House Sump
- Trenches
- Egnaro Aven
- Faulty Towers
- Wind Tunnel
- Speedwell Pot
- Buxton Water Sump
- Main Stream Passage
- White River Series
- Surprise View
- Crystal Inlet
- Main Stream Inlet
- Far Sump
- Boulder Hall
- Lake Passage
- Ink Sump
- Dooms Retreat

0 Feet 500
0 Metres 150

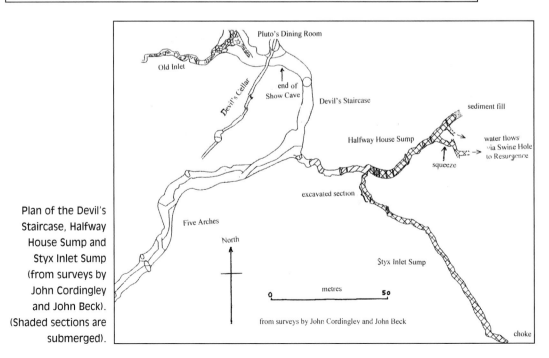

Plan of the Devil's Staircase, Halfway House Sump and Styx Inlet Sump (from surveys by John Cordingley and John Beck). (Shaded sections are submerged).

- Pluto's Dining Room
- Old Inlet
- end of Show Cave
- Devil's Cellar
- Devil's Staircase
- sediment fill
- Halfway House Sump
- water flows via Swine Hole to Resurgence
- squeeze
- excavated section
- Five Arches
- North
- Styx Inlet Sump
- metres 50
- from surveys by John Cordingley and John Beck
- choke

lights but difficulties caused by repeated flooding have necessitated closure of this former section of the show cave. Today, caving clubs can go beyond the tourist route in the winter months by arrangement and the trip into Far Peak makes a fine introduction to novice cavers.

The stream coming along the Five Arches flows away into a short branch passage at the Halfway House and after a sump 70m long it is blocked by a sediment fill, though scallop markings on the roof indicate previous high-velocity flow. The water re-appears in another impenetrable slot in the Swine Hole and flows on to the Resurgence in the Gorge. Whilst the link between Halfway House and Swine Hole is well established, all attempts to find a way through have failed and it is difficult to understand how the sediment fill was washed in. At the Halfway House diving has revealed that a low slot takes the flow to one side, which has been penetrated for 12m before it becomes too low. Before this point, in deep water, the Styx Inlet Sump admits water from a tube up to two metres high and a metre wide: it has been dived for 100m to a choke. The sediment on the floor includes items of domestic refuse probably derived from fly-tipping down shafts on the north-eastern sector of Dirtlow Rake. A notable feature of the Halfway House, Styx Inlet Sump and the Five Arches is the number of small joint caverns oriented north–south, at right angles to the mineral veins. Today the constricted nature of the Halfway House Sump causes water to back up in flood periods such as heavy rain

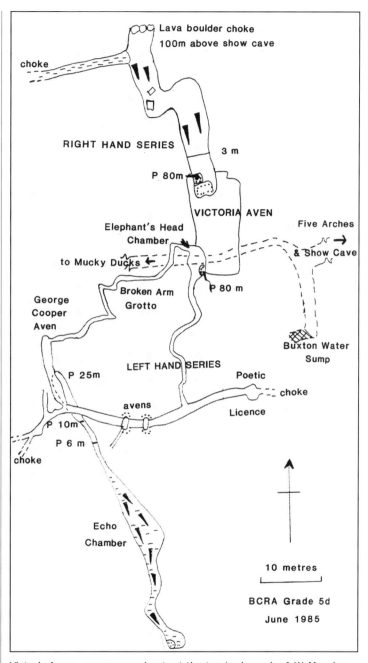

Victoria Aven – passages and pots at the top (redrawn by A.W. Marsden after preliminary surveys by G. Proudlove and R. Grimes).

or snow-melt: the backed-up water fills much of the Five Arches Passage and rises up the Devil's Staircase whence it overflows via the tourist cave, flooding Lumbago Walk to the roof: the latter is occasionally impassable for several hours or even days.

At the upstream end of the Five Arches (near the former end of the show cave) the stream enters from the left (south), rising from Buxton Water Sump, so named from the unlikely legend that

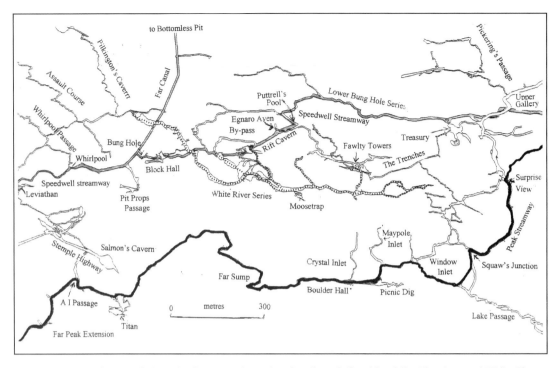

The central part of the Peak–Speedwell cave system, showing the relationship of the Kingdom and White River Series to the Peak streamway and to Speedwell Cavern's Far Canal and Bung Hole Series (from a compilation by John Beck). (Black shading = Peak Cavern streamway; Gray shading = Speedwell Cavern streamway; Dotted line = White River and Kingdom Series.)

the water came from Buxton – it does not! An early attempt at free-diving this in the 18th century resulted in the diver hitting his head on the submerged roof and knocking himself out – he was rescued with difficulty! First passed by cave-divers in 1949, the sump is over 100m long with an isolated rift chamber (Forward Halt 1, 57m high) partway and an unusual Torricellian Chamber just before it: here the water jets upward into a small rift chamber in such a way as to evacuate air bubbles and leave water at the negative depth of –1.5m! Beyond Buxton Water Sump is the magnificent stream cave of Far Peak, long suspected but first entered in 1949 by divers and by their helpers on the same day via the Mucky Ducks.

To the right at the end of the Five Arches another inlet passage leads to Victoria Aven, a chamber 80m high. It had been climbed by the lead miners who left a few wooden stemples wedged in the walls. Modern explorers have climbed the aven and found a short network of passages going north, terminating at a choke with fallen blocks of toadstone, derived from the Cavedale Lava. Two other passages met a "fossil" stream passage with a west–east trend, possibly a former extension of the White River series, and thence into a parallel series of fissure caverns, including Echo Rift. The latter does not extend to the same depth as Victoria Aven and is choked with sediment at the bottom.

Ahead, continuing beyond the foot of Victoria Aven, a short wade through the Wallows leads to a further section of stream passage with the Speedwell Pot in a passage off to one side. In flood conditions water rose from this 10m deep pot from Speedwell's Lower Bung Hole Series sump and flowed to the Five Arches to exit via the Peak Cavern Resurgence, but the pot was capped with concrete in a vain attempt to reduce flooding, and the flood water now rises up from Treasury Sump instead! Ahead a short crawl led to the end of exploration for Puttrell and his contemporaries in the early 20th century. It ended at an almost complete sump. In 1949 the divers' helpers managed to pass the obstacle, some by free-div-

ing whilst a separate party used hoses to siphon water out. Much digging at what became known as The Mucky Ducks has lowered the water level and access to Far Peak is nowadays by partial immersion for a few metres, with the water level only 20cm below the roof, a considerable improvement on the maximum of 2cm before digging began. In the roof above the approach to the Mucky Ducks is Perseverance Pot, which was reached by climbing a narrow passage from the Wallows. In the past unstable boulders have fallen from this Pot to cause the partial blockage damming up the Mucky Ducks.

After the Mucky Ducks, there is a comfortable hike up the Upper Gallery, a phreatic tube about 3m in diameter with a few branch passages. One is the Pick-

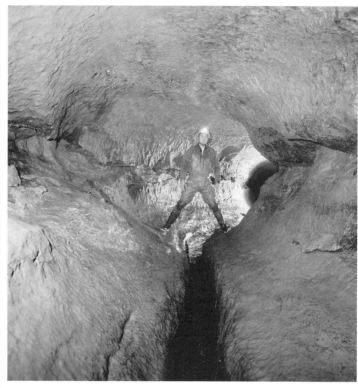

Upper Galley (P.D)

Mucky Ducks (P.D)

ering's Passage complex where in 1959 the student caver, Neil Moss, met his end in a fissure from which he could not escape. Above the fissure Moss Chamber is well decorated with stalactites. Together with the nearby Anniversary Hall, Cohesion Passage and Sump are vein cavities on two parallel minor east–west mineral veins. The end of Pickering's Passage is beneath Middle Bank Pot in the gulley on the surface but chokes have precluded a connection being made. It is possible that Middle Bank Pot is a long-abandoned swallet.

Returning to the Upper Gallery, it soon crosses a watershed with an aven to one side. It slopes down gently southwards with a narrow canyon in its floor, where there is a concealed sump which overflows to Surprise View occasionally. Surprise View is where, on the first exploration in 1949, the divers' helpers found themselves looking down on the divers 6m below. With an iron ladder now in place, today's explorers find this no obstacle and access is possible to the whole of the Far Peak Streamway, an unforgettable experience for novice cavers. The Upper Gallery has another major branch – a short hike to the Treasury Chamber, with a thick calcite pipe vein at its entrance. The Treasury was named from the cave pearls found by the first explorers, though they are no longer visible. On the left side of the Treasury a sloping pot with a 5m drop leads to a sump which connects with the bottom end of the Speedwell's Lower Bung Hole streamway after a dive 27m long. Flood water sometimes rises from Treasury Sump and overflows out via the Upper Gallery and Mucky Ducks. The Fawlty Towers dig in a mud-filled passage leading off Treasury Chamber eventually led to the Trenches at the top end of the Windpipe and thence to Liam's Way and Colostomy Crawl, where the connection was made to Egnaro Aven, an 18m climb from the Rift Cavern in Speedwell's Bung Hole Series. The Trenches bypass the tight tortuous crawl through Wind Tunnel, off Galena Chamber (see below), which had earlier provided an uncomfortable "dry land" link between Peak and Speedwell Caverns.

On the south side of the start of Liam's Way, a hole with a strong draft was dug out to reach a high aven. After two climbs up the Ventilator and Fever Pitches, and some 75m above the Trenches,

the extensive high-level series known as the White River Series was unexpectedly entered. These are "fossil" relics of an ancient stream cave system, with a classic keyhole profile of a phreatic tube in the roof of a vadose canyon, liberally decorated with stalactites, stalagmites, curtains and gour pools. Two main branches were linked by a crawl along Friday the Thirteenth Passage. The main system was some 500m long and unfortunately blocked at both ends. With its impressive grottoes parts received names such as the Kingdom, Pearly Gates and Heaven and tapes have been laid to protect the best speleothems! The White River Series lies partly on top of Speedwell's Bung Hole Series and its western end eventually crossesd over Speedwell's Far Canal to finish at a calcite-cemented choke not far from but higher than Pilkington's Cavern in Speedwell, hinting at a former continuation westwards. Two inlets admitted a small trickle of water which fell down a pothole in the floor. The White River Series had several other pots in the floor almost making contact between Peak and Speedwell Caverns. One ended at a choke directly above mine workings in the Bung Hole Series – working upwards the old lead miners had come close to a breakthrough but never completed it. Another hole in the floor had five pitches totalling over 80m taking a stream down to the level of the main streamway. It was named the Moosetrap, taken from Dave Nixon's nickname of Moose as he fell down the Fifth Pitch and had difficulty getting out! A flat-out crawl from the western end

of the Series was dug out and found to lead to the top of Block Hall in Speedwell Cavern's Bung Hole Series.

Passing by the entrance to Treasury Passage, the Upper Gallery soon rises to a watershed at a partial blockage of boulders cemented by flowstone with a group of stalactites above. On the right is Watershed Aven, an isolated rift chamber. Beyond the Watershed the original phreatic tube declines gently and a narrow vadose trench is incised into the floor. In flood conditions water rises from a concealed slot and flows to Surprise View. Descent of the trench leads to Surprise View with its 6m ladder into the main Far Peak Streamway. Just before the ladder a branch passage on the right leads to a series of muddy crawls eventually linking with passages above the Squaws Junction inlet (see below).

The Far Peak Streamway caverns are impressive at over a kilometre long, in places 20m high and 10m wide, with the classic keyhole profile of a phreatic tube above a vadose canyon. The present stream is a misfit, much smaller than the energetic stream which eroded the canyon in past millennia. The streamway has been developed as the focal part of a dendritic stream cave system on a guiding bedding plane some 14m above a similar bedding plane in Speedwell Cavern. Indeed part of the Peak streamway crosses over the Speedwell's. Downstream from the iron ladder the vadose canyon shallows to a drained phreatic tube where the Far Peak streamway ends at the inner end of Buxton Water sump, with a

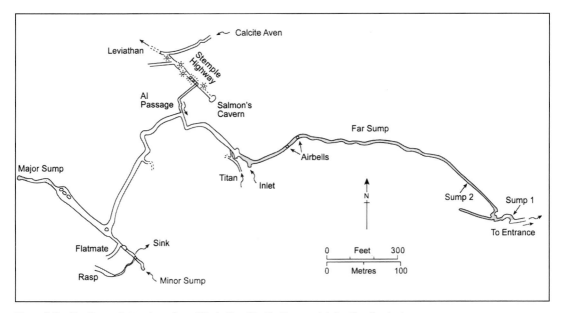

Plan of the Far Sump Extensions (modified after Martin Farr and John Cordingley).

tight inlet passage to the south only explored for a few metres so far.

Upstream from the Surprise View ladder, the streamway reaches Squaws Junction, named by the three divers on the first exploration who referred to their wives as squaws. An inlet stream cascades down a slope of about 4m with a series of muddy passages above. The inlet came from a bedding plane barely 2cm high: later this was blocked with wooden wedges and the water squirted out round the corner and gradually washed away some of the mud fill, yielding a crawl connection to the Window Inlet in the Main Stream Passage. To the north a complex series of muddy crawls curves back via Wigwam Aven and Galena Chamber to the Upper Gallery just above Surprise View. At the top of Wigwam Aven a very small vadose passage (the M1) winds its way to Disappointment Rift. A dig here led eventually to a connection back to

Galena Chamber. A branch led to several subsidiary rifts which were later climbed to reach a short passage close to the White River Series but no way through has been found. Another branch was the Wind Tunnel; with a strong draft the body-tight crawl reached the Trenches, but the opening of the Fawlty Towers dig from the Treasury bypassed the need to struggle up Wind Tunnel.

Turning left at Squaws Junction, another stream enters the main streamway from Lake Passage on the left (south); it can be followed to Lake Sump, once a 5m long sump but now a lengthy duck with little air-space; it can be bypassed through a tight muddy crawl to the right into a continuation of the stream passage, which ends at Ink Sump after another 50m, with the Ramp chamber rising high above. Divers have explored Ink Sump for some 160m and dug through a submerged choke to climb into Dooms Retreat, a boulder-

choked fissure in a mineral vein close to Dirtlow Rake. Water-tracing experiments have shown the drainage from the fluorspar opencast workings on Dirtlow Rake enters the Peak Cavern system here.

Past the Lake Passage inlet, the main streamway becomes rather muddy with a trickle of a stream which rises from the foot of a boulder slope. A climb up this leads to Boulder Hall with its floor of collapsed boulders. At the top of the slope a climb to the left leads to the mud-choked Picnic Dig. Not far beyond Boulder Hall, a hole in the roof has been climbed for about 60m to Crystal Inlet passage with fine stalactite formations and a sediment choke at the end. The main passage then gradually closes down to Far Sump. The ancient collapse which floors Boulder Hall has blocked the drainage and the floor from Boulder Hall to Far Sump is composed of thick silt and sand deposits which have dammed

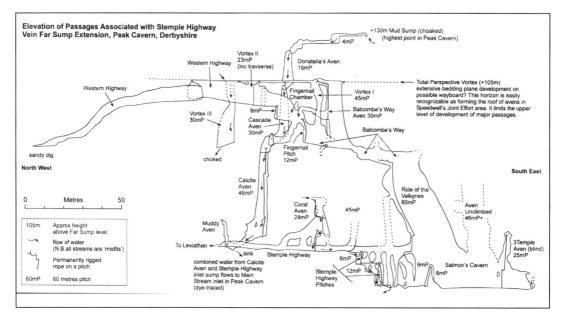

Stemple Highway (after a compilation by John Cordingley).

up the 385m long Far Sump. The choked upper ends of Crystal and Maypole Inlets and the stream above Squaws Junction hint at the presence of a separate stream cave sub-parallel to the main streamway, almost entirely filled with sediment.

After several attempts Far Sump was eventually dived by Martin Farr for a distance of 385m to rise into Far Peak Extension (also known as Far Sump Extension) with some 500m of dry passages. A surprising find was the miner's initials "AI" scratched onto a rock by a branch passage, demonstrating that the old miners had reached the Extension without penetrating either the Far Peak Caverns or Far Sump. The Extension had two further sumps, Major and Minor. Major Sump had a submerged mineral vein but diving failed to find a way on. Diving in Minor Sump reached a tight series of passages leading to the Rasp. AI Passage branched off Far Peak Extension

and led into Stemple Highway, a complex series of phreatic tube passages and vein cavities along a thin mineral vein trending north-west. The caverns have been climbed to a wayboard 105m above the streamway. Donatella's Aven rises still higher above the wayboard to reach a total height of 130m above the streamway. At the south-east end of Stemple Highway is Salmon's Cavern where rotten stemples confirm the former presence of the old miners. They were set in the south-east wall but the miners made little attempt to exploit the vein. A climb of some 50m up the east wall failed to find a way onwards. At the north-western end of Stemple Highway a passage trending north-east led into Calcite Aven with a 5m wide vein of large calcite crystals; fallen blocks of calcite litter the floor. A high-level inlet off Stemple Highway was Western Highway, which ended in a choke not far from Joint Effort at the top of

Speedwell's Cliff Cavern. Another choke at the north-western end of Stemple Highway was full of what turned out to be miners' waste; it was later dug out to provide a dry route to the foot of Leviathan, thereby demonstrating that this had been the original miners' route into Far Peak Extension; today it yields a link to Speedwell Cavern's streamway (see separate chapter). The massive Titan Cavern was found by climbing up through a choke of massive boulders in a short passage to the south of the inner end of Far Sump (see separate chapter).

Most of the stream in Far Sump comes from a submerged inlet trending southeast some 15m from the western end of Far Sump; this has been dived for 55m to a choke roughly beneath Titan. Off Minor Sump a narrow passage leads into the parallel Rasp Passage in an irregular NW–SE mineral vein; this delivers a small stream which usually sinks again to re-appear at the inlet in Far Sump: in flood conditions it overflows via AI Passage and thence into Far Sump. Upstream, the Rasp has been dived through three sumps to a constriction which has not been passed despite valiant pumping efforts. Flatmate is a tiny passage close to the beginning of Minor Sump Passage: it has been pushed for over 60m, currently ending close to the projected line of the Rasp Passage.

Far Sump is the limit of exploration for the ordinary caver, but there are three other delights for the climber – high in the roof near Boulder Chamber is Crystal Aven with a short passage leading north to a clay blockage. Close to the top of the climb up to Boulder Rift is a short branch going south-east known as Picnic Dig; it is blocked by mud fill but in spite of much digging little progress has been made. At the foot of the boulder slope Maypole Inlet was reached with the aid of a scaffolding pole system (later a set of ladders) and led northwards to a muddy series of passages which have been dug out for about 100m: the inner end of these meets the clay-filled passages which appear to link with the Trenches leading back to Treasury Chamber.

Much of Far Peak and its Extension lie beneath the upper parts of Cavedale and its adjacent slopes, but no direct connection between cave and dale has been found. The dry valley of Cavedale was evidently eroded when the ground was frozen during the latter part of the Ice Age, whilst the deeper ground remained unfrozen and transmitted meltwater via the network of caves.

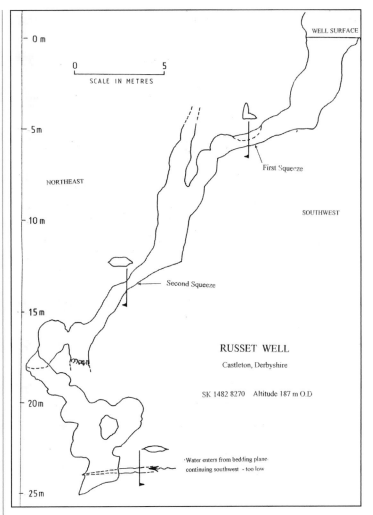

Profile of Russet Well (by John Cordingley).

A few Uranium Series dates have been determined: one is on a fallen block of flowstone in the main canyon, presumably derived from the phreatic tube in the roof where it was deposited in mid-Devensian times, some 51,000 to 59,000 years ago (see Speleogenesis chapter).

The sheet of basalt known as the Cavedale Lava is inter-layered within the limestone succession and forms an umbrella impeding the percolation of surface drainage into much of Peak Cavern's streamway, except where there are fractures, hence the scarcity of speleothems. In contrast the profusion of stalactites and flowstone in the White River Series can be explained by the Lava having died out northwards so that direct percolation is possible. The Lava also seems to thin out westwards and only thin representatives have been seen in JH Mine and Titan.

Returning to the Vestibule and the gorge outside, their form suggests that they were the site of a deep Vauclusian spring with water rising from the phreatic zone

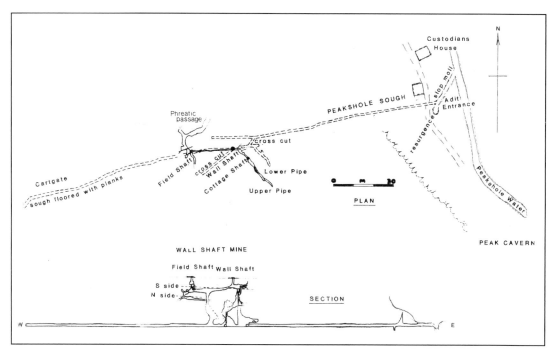

Plan and section of Peaks Hole Sough (from a survey by D. Penney and D. Jackson, modified by D.G. Quirk).

to overflow over a lip when the floor of Hope Valley was much higher than at present. The corollary of this is that much of the Peak Cavern cave system was then deep in the phreatic zone and has been partially drained as Hope Valley has been progressively eroded deeper.

Russet Well and Slop Moll are two springs on either side of the entrance to Peak Cavern Gorge. Together they are the main resurgences for the Speedwell Cavern stream and, in flood conditions, for some of Peak Cavern's drainage. Russet Well is in a poorly defined NE–SW mineral vein, mostly calcite with a little sphalerite (zinc ore). It has been dived to a depth of around 25m, inclining steeply eastwards

with two awkward constrictions. The water enters from a bedding plane going south-west but it is too low for divers to penetrate. As the well is on the east side of the Gorge and its water comes from Speedwell Cavern to the west, the water rising there has passed beneath the Peakshole stream. On the other side of the Peak Cavern stream, i.e. to the south-west, Slop Moll is a spring obviously connected to Russet Well as their water levels vary in accord, but it is choked with boulders and cannot be explored.

Peakshole Sough and Wall Shaft Mine are in the western wall of the entrance to the Gorge, above and to the west of Slop Moll. The entrance to the

sough (a more or less horizontal tunnel excavated for the purposes of draining a mine or mines) is directly above Slop Moll but there seems to be no connection. The sough was driven roughly 250m WSW along two thin veins. Workings in the roof connect with Wall Shaft under the wall along the foot of Cowlow. Pipe workings extend about 30m SE from Wall Shaft. Further west there is short mud-choked cave passage extending to the north. The relationship of pipe vein and cave to either Peak or Speedwell cave systems is not known. An ephemeral spring in the field west of Goosehill Hall discharges a substantial stream in flood conditions and may be connected to the cave in Peakshole Sough.

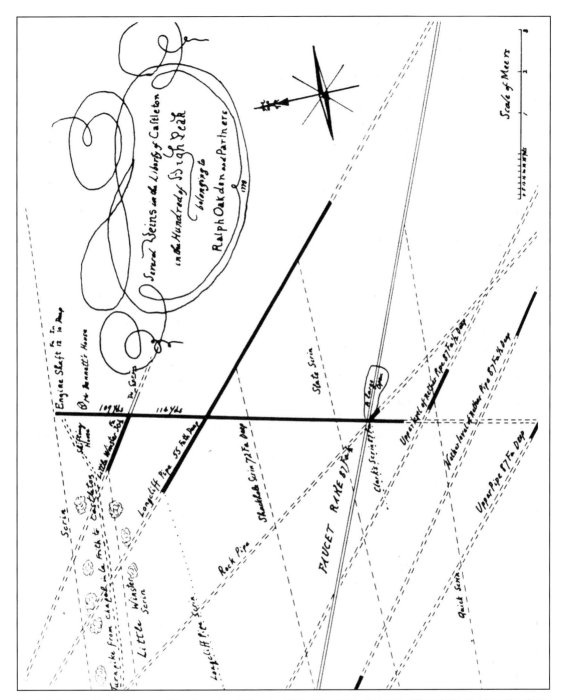

Ralph Oakden & Partners plan of the Speedwell Mine in 1779. (The scale of meers differs from the lengths given along the canal!).

workings and caverns suggest that there are more mine workings now under water but details are unknown. Above water level the series of caverns in Longcliffe Vein extends to beneath the road in the Winnats Pass though they are deep enough so as to cause no alarm, as the highest point is more than 40m below the road.

There are hints in the few contemporary descriptions that the tunnel was flooded to waist depth during mining, much as it is today, which raises ques-

John Mawe's section of 1802 from Mam Tor (on the right), through Treak Cliff and Blue John mines (centre) to Longcliffe and Speedwell Mine (left). (W = Winnats Pass; S = Speedwell; X = Little Winster Vein; V = immense opening; N = Longcliffe Rakes; K = Faucet Rake; H = a small rake or scrin; R = Rock Pipe).

tions about both the source and exit of excess water. Under mild flood conditions water enters from fissures beneath the steps and some excess water may be lost into Longcliffe Vein. There are also questions about the drilling techniques in a flooded level, where it is possible that the miners left a rock sill at intervals and worked in the dry ahead of it before blasting it away and then repeating the procedure. A boat carried the waste rock back to the shaft, whence it was hauled to the surface until the Bottomless Pit Cavern was breached and provided a suitable depository for waste rock from the Far Canal. The second half of the First Canal crosses two more mineral veins but they are too thin to exploit. The canal tunnel also has two alcoves: one is close to the Halfway House and is said to have housed a bellows for ventilation – operated by a boy on his own. The other alcove is said to be a safety hole where miners could shelter when blasting further along the tunnel.

The mineral veins in Speedwell Mine are dominated by calcite, with minor amounts of baryte, fluorite (blue or yellow) and

The Bottomless Pit Cavern (P.D)

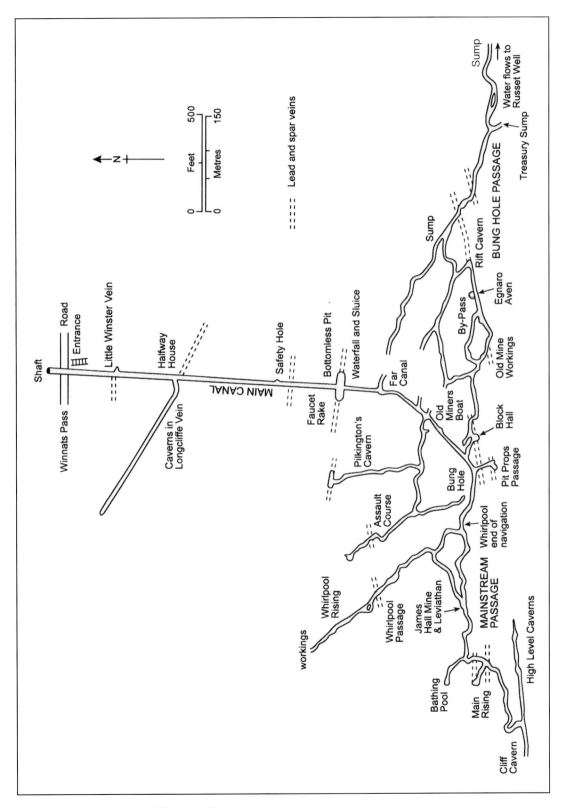

General plan of the Speedwell Mine and Caverns.

Castleton Caves

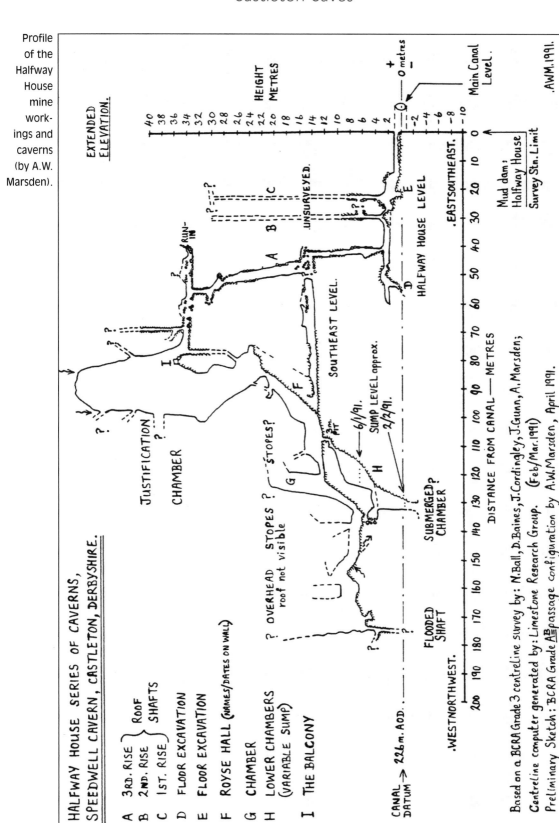

Profile of the Halfway House mine workings and caverns (by A.W. Marsden).

32

Cavedale – the amphitheatre lies above the Great Cave in Peak Cavern (P.D)

The Great Cave in
Peak Cavern (P.D)

Diving in Buxton Water
Sump, Peak Cavern (J.N.C)

Peakshole Water
Resurgence (J.N.C)

Five Arches (T.D.F)

Above: Peak Cavern Streamway
phreatic tube (P.D)

Left: Stalactites at
Watershed Aven (P.D)

Peak Cavern vadose canyon
(T.D.F)

Far Stump (T.D.F)

Squaws Junction in Peak Cavern (P.D)

The main streamway at Squaws Junction (P.D)

Lake Passage Inlet
(T.D.F)

Boulder Hall in Peak Cavern (J.N.C)

Inner end of Far Peak Sump (J.N.C)

Stalactite formations in the White River Series (P.D)

White River Series (P.D)

Russet Well (P.D)

Boats passing in the Halfway House in Speedwell Mine (P.D)

The Lake in the Bottomless Pit (P.D)

Swimming across the Whirlpool (P.D)

Main streamway in mild flood condition in Speedwell Cavern (P.D)

The Leaning Tower in the Main Speedwell streamway (P.D)

Whirlpool Rising – the water rises and falls by 60cm in mild flood conditions (A.M)

Pilkington's Cavern (R.P.S)

Block Hall in Speedwell
Cavern (P.D)

Far Flats in Nettle Pot
(P.D)

Miners' Workshop in JH Mine (P.D)

Long By-pass inlet, Speedwell Cavern (P.D)

Descending Leviathan, JH Mine (P.D)

The vast Titan Cavern (P.D)

Lord Mulgrave's Dining Room in Blue John Cavern (P.D)

The vast Variegated Cavern in Blue John Cavern (P.D)

The Fairy Grotto in Blue John Cavern (P.D)

Stalactites in the Dream Cave, Treak Cliff Cavern (P.D)

Garlands Pot in Giant's Hole
(P.D)

The Crabwalk in Giant's Hole
(P.D)

Oxlow Caverns in Oxlow Cavern (P.D)

Elizbeth Shaft
Nettle Pot (P.D)

Giants Hole entrance (T.D.F)

Gravel cemented by flowstone near
Base Camp Chamber (T.D.F)

Boss Aven, Giants Hole (P.D)

Salmon's Cavern, par sump extension in Peak Cavern (P.D)

Main Chamber in Eldon
Hole (P.D)

Millers Chamber in
Eldon Hole (P.D)

Eldon Hole (T.D.F)

Eldon quarry fissure with
sediment fill (T.D.F)

Odin Mine entrance (P.D)

The Speedwell Mine and Cavern

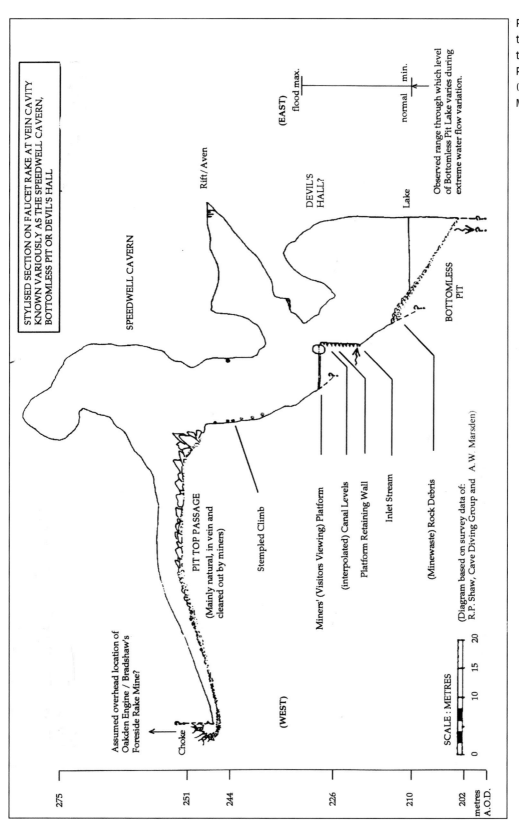

Profile of the Bottomless Pit Cavern (by A.W. Marsden).

galena as early phases of mineral deposition; indeed some exposures of the veins contain negligible galena. Faucet Rake in the Bottomless Pit Cavern had so little lead ore that it was not worked at platform level. There are pyrite inclusions in the calcite, sometimes oxidized to goethite (iron hydroxide). Minute crystals of the rare mineral wulfenite (lead molybdate) have been found in the Whirlpool Passage. Yellow fluorite occurs in Little Winster Vein and there are thin layers of baryte and blue fluorite in Whirlpool Passage's pipe veins. The stopes in the Bung Hole Series are irregular masses largely of calcite instead of a fissure vein, though nearby New Rake forms a distinct vein to both east and west of the stopes.

The First Canal tunnel ends at the Bottomless Pit Cavern, which is the end of the tourist route today and was once known as Devil's Hall. At this point visitors are about 170m below the surface, and they can step out onto a platform built across the cavern, but when the miners reached it they looked out into open space from some 15m above a sloping floor, beyond which there is a lake 13m in diameter set off to

Wreck of Miners' boat in the Far Canal (P.D)

the east. Above the canal tunnels rises the great cavern in the mineral vein known as Faucet or Foreside Rake, which closes to a dome 50m above the platform. It is an unsolved problem as to whether the miners knew the cavern was there beforehand and aimed for it directly, with the aid of some careful surveying, or whether it was pure chance that they met it. On the surface high above the vein was worked from Bradshaw's Grove. The miners climbed the west side of the cavern with the aid of wooden stemples set into the rock like the rungs of a ladder. Some 22m above the platform a level was driven westwards in Faucet Rake for about 50m, where it ends in a choke of fallen boulders and vein minerals, mostly calcite, which might conceal a former access route from higher mine workings. Opposite the platform, directly above the Pit is an inclined rift which soon closes up.

It is logical that where the platform is today there was originally an aqueduct so that boats could cross directly into the Far Canal on the other side. Also they would be able to unload waste rock directly into the Pit if they could pull alongside it. The aqueduct was filled in when it became a tourist cavern, but a culvert and sluices were left beneath the platform and permit water to flow from the canals to make a spectacular waterfall into the Bottomless Pit on the east side. The Pit is 16m deep onto a slope of boulders with the lake beyond. The lake is floored by boulders and miners' waste from the Far Canal, partly covered by silt. A fissure in the north wall soon closes up. The water has been traced using

dyes, which are said to reappear at Russet Well in Castleton about 23 hours later. As the water level at Russet Well is 12m lower than in the Bottomless Pit there must be a free-running stream cavern somewhere between but it has not yet been found by explorers. It is not known whether the old miners had entered this theoretical cavern.

The ordinary visitors' tour ends at the Bottomless Pit, but occasional parties of cavers can explore the very interesting passages beyond – if they are prepared to get wet through by wading along the Far Canal and swimming across the Whirlpool.

The only surviving contemporary mine plan was drawn for Ralph Oakden & partners. Dated 1779, it shows the Far Canal having been driven about 150 yards south of the Bottomless Pit, which is inexplicably shown on the wrong side. The plan has a scale bar which differs from measurements written alongside the canal! It also shows several mineral veins it was expected to intersect, notably the Upper, Nether and Lower Levels of a "pipe vein", curiously at similar depths of 87 or 87½ fathoms (about 160m), broadly comparable with the depth of the canal beneath the surface, around 190m. None of these pipe veins has been entered by modern explorers and their location remains an unsolved mystery. Since the pipes were shown on Oakden's plan as expected to be reached in the future he must have been aware of them and there ought to have been a way down to these deep mine workings from the surface, but nothing is known of this route. Both

Engraving of the
Bottomless Pit (from
Martel, 1897).

Engraving of the Bottomless Pit (from Martel, 1897).

a "Rock Pipe" trending south-east and Clark's Scrin trending west–south-west from the Bottomless Pit cavern are shown on Oakden's plan; Rock Pipe also appears on Mawe's section as a nearly vertical vein, contradictory to the usual definition of a pipe. However, no evidence of either vein can be seen today and it is not known what they were.

A section through the hill and along the canals drawn by John Mawe in 1802 shows the mineral veins to be inclined and crossing – a pattern not supported by modern exploration. Mawe's section does not extend far enough to the south to show the pipe veins of Oakden's plan.

The Far Canal bends to the south-west just past the limit shown on Oakden's plan of 1779. Near the bend the canal tunnel intersected three low cave passages but these have been walled up on the left (downstream side) to maintain the water level and only flood waters escape there. Opposite one of the walled-up swallets there is a body-tight crawl passage on the right, later found to lead to Pilkington's Cavern, of which more will be said later. Nearer the Bung Hole, the Far Canal swings almost due west, parallel to but a few metres north of New Rake. At the Bung Hole the miners met the stream caverns at slightly above the right level to yield their desired canal haulage system and a dam 6m high was built to maintain the water level. The canal tunnel continues almost to the Whirlpool, parallel to and a few

metres north of New Rake. At the Bung Hole dam a plug hole and bung were installed to drain off water when necessary, hence the name. The Bung itself was a tapered length of tree trunk! Much later, in the 1920s, a rubber motor tyre was used as a washer to reduce leakage! Below the dam wall the stream caverns continue eastwards for about 700 metres – more of that later. Apart from the dam the canal tunnel was well designed at the required altitude. Modern investigations have revealed that there were at least two routes from the hilltop into the stream caverns known before

the canal intersected them (see the section on Pilkington's Cavern below, and the chapter on Leviathan). Surveying from the surface down to the caverns and down the hillside to where the shaft was sunk established the right level for the canal before work began, but none of the survey documents survive.

Waste rock from the Far Canal tunnel was transported by boat and tipped down into the Bottomless Pit. Estimates vary but around 3,000 to 4,000 tons were produced, calculated on the volume of the Far Canal. The traditional guide's tale says

40,000 tons but where this figure comes from is not known. The waste rock was disposed of in the Bottomless Pit to avoid the necessity of hauling such a load to the surface. The sunken wreck of a miners' barge still lies in the Far Canal. Propulsion was by pulling on pegs stuck into the wall. The waste rock has partly choked the underwater outlet to the lake in the Bottomless Pit and cave-divers have not been able to explore downstream. Under normal conditions water drains away through the blockage, but flood waters can occasionally back up to platform level and even fill both canal tunnels.

Beyond the Bung Hole the artificial canal tunnel gradually merges with the stream caverns and from near the Whirlpool it is an entirely natural passage, the main Speedwell streamway. There is one short branch into mine workings in New Rake, known today as Pit Props Passage, though the props do not support the roof: wooden posts were placed there to hold planks to make a dam to retain water during a drought in the 1920s. Deep water conceals the submerged stream passage. A climb at the end of Pit Props Passage leads into stopes (vein cavities?) thought to be in New Rake, but possibly including the closely parallel Horsepit Rake. The Whirlpool takes its name from the fact that both the branch passage to the north-west and the Main Stream Passage emit streams and where they meet the eddy is liable to swirl swimmers around – the pool is 2.5m deep and crossing it requires a short swim of about 10m aided by a rope strung across the pool.

The Speedwell Cavern's stream caves are a classic example of a dendritic network of phreatic tubes developed on a single bedding plane. Inception was by solution along that bedding plane with a thin shale parting while the limestone massif was still deep below the water table. As water levels fell in consequence of the erosional deepening of Hope Valley, free-running streams along the floor of the tube network carried abrasive sand and boulders along and eroded canyon-like vadose conduits. In an ideal situation one should be able to follow the stream passage up to where the water sinks, but in the Speedwell all the streams rise from sumps in fissures or mineral veins, coming from submerged cave systems as yet only explored by divers for a short distance.

The Main Stream Passage is a classic phreatic tube in the roof with a vadose canyon below developed along a bedding plane in the limestones some 14m below the guiding bedding plane in Peak Cavern. The stream passage can be followed westwards rising slowly upstream. It is about 2m high at first but gradually rises to around 8m high and 4m wide. About halfway up the 400m streamway, it is partly blocked by the Boulder Piles, massive fallen rocks. Above them are two holes in the roof filled with large boulders with the remains of timbers placed by the miners to stabilize them. A small passage on one side was choked with miners' rubble but it was dug out and explored in the 1990s and provided a bypass to the boulder-filled holes, enabling explorers to reach a vast cavern in New Rake. The cavern was first recorded by the Cam-

bridge student James Plumptre in 1793 and is now known as Leviathan; mine workings high in its wall yielded much lead ore. Leviathan had also been reached by 18th-century miners from James Hall Over Engine Mine on the surface some 170m above. In the Speedwell's Main Stream Passage the miners built a plankway above the stream as far as the Boulder Piles: notches which held the cross-beams can still be seen. Sledge-like corves were used to transport lead ore from workings off Leviathan down to the boats at the Whirlpool.

Beyond the Boulder Piles there are wide sand banks, Blackpool Sands, where sediment deposited during floods is an indicator of what can be transported from the swallets through the flooded zone leading to the Main Rising. A few large boulders hamper progress, including one tilted across the passage and known as the Leaning Tower. A ladder provides access to a branch passage about 100m long high in the right-hand (north) wall which ends at the Bathing Pool – a circular cavern about 6m wide and entirely flooded; cave-divers have found that the water is 25m deep to a constriction. A chimney in the roof is choked with flowstone 12m up. Swimming and diving have failed to find any further way on though a trickling streamlet overflows, presumably fed from an underwater inlet. In an alcove a few metres before the Bathing Pool, Secret Sump has also been explored by diving to a depth of 41m. As the water levels of the two sumps are different it seems that they are not connected underwater, and both water levels are some 6m above

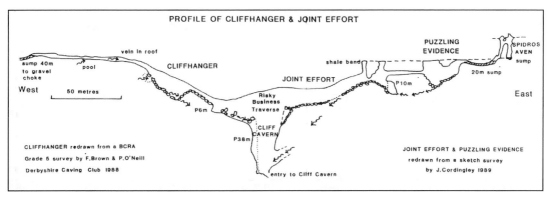

Profile of Cliff Cavern, Joint Effort and Cliffhanger (compiled by John Cordingley).

the main stream level.

Shortly after the Bathing Pool passage, there is another branch to the left, Cliff Cavern Passage, easily accessible up a 2m waterfall over a thin mineral vein which appears to be a poor representative of Horsepit Rake. But before exploring this it is worth going some 50m further upstream to the Main Rising, a phreatic lift where the stream rises at an altitude of 240m from a flooded pothole 36m deep. Divers have explored this and an up-and-down submerged passage for some 250m to the south-west to the deep Doux de Castleton, which leads into New Leviathan Rift at a

depth of 72m, where further diving is precluded by the water rising from a sediment-choked slot; floods wash out some of this but it slumps back when water pressure drops. Dye tests have shown that the water comes from Giants Hole, about a kilometre to the north-west, and from the other Rushup Edge swallets some 2 to 3km further away, as well as from the Coalpithole lead mines near Perryfoot some 4km away. As the altitudes of the lowest accessible water levels in both the swallets and the Main Rising are similar, 240m O.D., a long, deep, submerged U-tube system must lie beneath the limestone plateau

to the west of the Speedwell stream caverns. Occasionally, and I have only seen this once, the Main Rising ebbs and flows, rising by a metre or so, and the excess water is then dammed up behind the Boulder Piles to a depth of 3m, falling back to normal within half an hour or so, before the process is repeated an hour later.

Returning to the last branch passage on the left, Cliff Cavern Passage, the short climb leads into a small cavern with the Miners' Toast scrawled on the wall: *A Health to all Miners and Mentainers of Mines; October 20th 1781, J.B., M.N.* This is

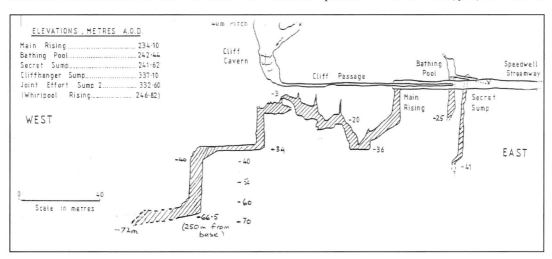

Profile of Speedwell's Main Rising (by John Cordingley).

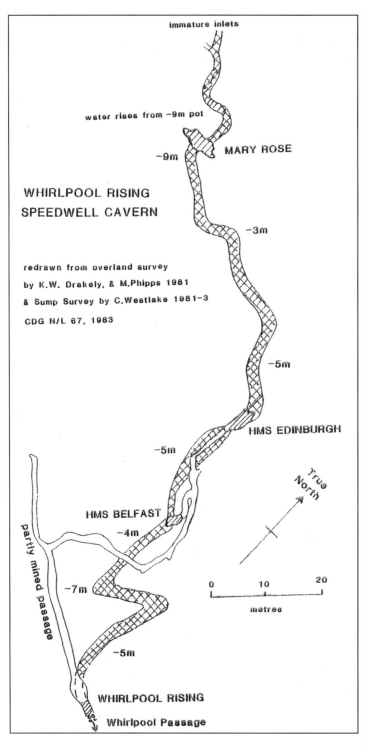

immature inlets

water rises from −9m pot

−9m

MARY ROSE

WHIRLPOOL RISING
SPEEDWELL CAVERN

−3m

redrawn from overland survey
by K.W. Drakely, & M.Phipps 1981
& Sump Survey by C.Westlake 1981-3

CDG N/L 67, 1983

−5m

−5m

HMS EDINBURGH

True North

HMS BELFAST

−4m

partly mined passage

−7m

0   10   20

metres

−5m

WHIRLPOOL RISING

Whirlpool Passage

Plan of Whirlpool Rising (compilation by A.W. Marsden).

known that Joseph Bennet and Matthew Nall were active miners then, so perhaps they are the ones who "signed on". Many other names and initials have been scratched into the mud coating the wall, mostly explorers over the last century, though the practice is frowned on today. A bicentenary toast to the old lead miners was drunk there in October 1981.

Past the Miners' Toast, Cliff Cavern Passage continues for some 150m, sometimes so low as to require crawling. A branch passage is completely full of bedded silts. The passage then enters the bottom of the vast high Cliff Cavern, with a short branch passage awaiting digging out. A scramble up a massive boulder slope reaches a terrace at the foot of twin waterfalls cascading down the nearly vertical wall on the far side. The cavern has been climbed for more than 40m to reach high rift passages extending to east and west, named Joint Effort and Cliffhanger respectively. Each is the source of one of the waterfalls and each extends for some 170m. To the west is an impenetrable sump, whilst to the east a small sump was dived to reach narrow fissures. The rifts follow a thin mineral vein but no evidence was found that the old miners had reached it. The foot of Cliff Cavern is the usual end of the trip for visiting parties of cavers, but there are some branches worth seeing on the way back. Whirlpool Passage is the most important of these.

From the Whirlpool a gently

probably the date when the canal tunnel was completed and the miners could enter the stream caverns without the laborious

descent from the hilltop. It is uncertain who JB and MN were, but they could evidently write (most miners could not); however, it is

rising walking-size passage trends north-west. It is a phreatic tube with vadose canyon in shape, as are all the Speedwell's stream caves. After some 90m of comfortable walking, Whirlpool Passage opens out into a chamber 3m high and wide with a short mine level in the roof back above the streamway. There are signs of mining activity here with hollows in the roof where lead ore and gangue minerals have been chiselled out, and at one side are the remains of a platform where ore was crushed and sorted. Notches in the walls just above the stream indicate that there was once a plankway for corves to be dragged down to the boats at the Whirlpool, though the workings visible today hardly seem to be enough to justify the labour. Beyond the small cavern Whirlpool Passage gets lower with the stream entering from a short oxbow on the left. Ahead is a dry crawl back to the stream and there are holes in the roof choked with rock chippings. Perhaps this was where the miners climbed up into Nether Pipe, though if the depth of 87½ fathoms on Oakden's plan is correct it suggests that those pipe workings may have been higher. Thus, digging out the chippings might lead up to Nether Pipe.

Whirlpool Rising is a few metres ahead, with the stream rising from a pool some two metres in diameter. There is a short mined passage above, ending where it meets a mineral vein thought to be either Faucet Rake or Quick Scrin branching off it to the south-west; however, the miners made little attempt to work it. Whirlpool Rising has been dived for 122m to the north, reaching

three small air-bells (above-water chambers); two of these can also be reached by a tight crawl from the mine tunnel above the rising: the last chamber is close to Faucet Rake, with the water rising from a boulder choke at a depth of 11m in a submerged vein cavity.

Whirlpool Rising has an unusual characteristic – it ebbs and flows after wet weather. I have watched the water surface rise by some 60cm in about a minute: the excess water flows off down the passage as a wave of comparable height for another minute or two; then it falls back to its starting level and the cycle is repeated about every four minutes. The wave coming down Whirlpool Passage can be alarming to cavers who do not know about it! The explanation appears to be some form of siphon action in the as yet unexplored passages beyond. Dye tests have shown that, like Main Rising, the water comes from Giants Hole and the other Rushup Edge swallets, with a contribution from Winnats Head Cave. Occasionally floods cause the principal flow to switch from Main to Whirlpool Rising, and later back again. This may be due to the floods temporarily moving sandbanks in the inaccessible submerged passages beyond. However, in some drought periods Whirlpool Passage can be almost dry. In spite of the hydrological connection Whirlpool Rising is some 8m higher than Main Rising so there should be open cave passage somewhere upstream.

There are two branches off Whirlpool Passage: one leads back to the Main Stream Cavern near the Boulder Piles; the other

The foot of the Bung Hole wall (P.D)

was full of sediment until dug out in the 1980s: it is known as Troubled Waters and links to the Assault Course streamway in the Pilkington's Cavern system (see below).

As mentioned above there is a body-sized crawl passage off the Far Canal near the Bung Hole. I first dug this out in 1943 and crawled flat-out for 30m before it opened into a small vadose streamway about 2m high. A little further on this opened into a cavern about 3m wide and 15m high. Large timbers were wedged in the wall, and in the roof high above the remains of a wooden platform could be seen, showing that the old lead miners had been there earlier. This could only be part of the route described by James Pilkington in 1789. In the 1970s, with the aid of a battery-powered drill and Rawlbolts, this was climbed by Richard Shaw and a meandering passage led to climbs up a series of nearly vertical fissures, called Round, Galena, Chain and Waterfall Pitches, eventually leading into Mud Hall and Watricle Cavern,

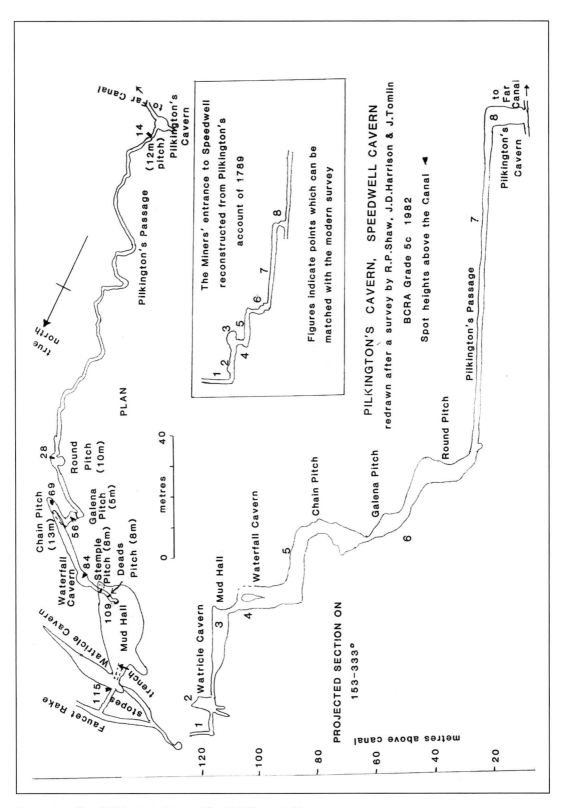

Plan and profile of Pilkington's Cavern (after R.P. Shaw et al.).

120m above canal level (watricle is an old term for stalactite formations). The depths and distances roughly correspond with Pilkington's figures, confirming that this was the cavern he had described nearly two centuries earlier. The miners had processed ore from Faucet Rake in Watricle Cavern and at the side was the foot of a collapsed mineshaft: surveying showed this was directly below a choked shaft on the surface 50m above, possibly Tellyer's Venture. Pilkington's account gave distances and depths but unfortunately no compass bearings so it was impossible to work out the location of his cavern from his description alone. Pilkington noted that miners had been down to "near a point where the level now driving was expected". Though published in 1789, his account referred to mining activities at least ten years earlier when the canal tunnels were being driven, and it supports the hypothesis that the miners knew beforehand that their tunnel would intersect the stream caverns. Sulivan's account of 1780 came to the same conclusion, though it is less detailed.

Flowstone from high in the Pilkington's Series has yielded uranium series dates of 91,000 to 115,000 years BP, i.e. deposited in the Ipswichian interglacial (see Speleogenesis chapter). A fallen block of flowstone near the Rift Cavern in the Bung Hole Series also gave a date of 96,000 years BP: the block had possibly come from the White River Series of Peak Cavern though the miners evidently never made the connection. As stalactites only grow in air-filled caves these show that water levels had fallen to near canal level by the Ipswichian Inter-

glacial.

Beyond Pilkington's Cavern the access passage continues to another stream cave trending north-west, which became known as the Assault Course owing to wedged boulders making progress awkward. The small stream cave was just about walking height at first but soon deteriorated to a flat-out crawl. Later this was dug out to reach another unsuspected cavern on the line of the Quick Scrin branch off Faucet Rake. The small stream may have its origin in the trickle which sinks near the bend in the Winnats Pass; also sandstone pebbles suggest a former inlet there bringing material in from Rushup Edge. A branch passage off the Assault Course was full of sediment and it was dug out to provide a link to Whirlpool Passage known as Troubled Waters. Although this may have been open in mining days, it is doubtful if it was their original route into the stream cave system; it is more likely that the lower end of the Assault Course streamway was open to what is now the Bung Hole Series before the canal tunnel breached them. The downstream end of the Assault Course is now blocked by miners' debris and submerged by the waters of the Far Canal.

As noted above, the main stream cave was dammed at the Bung Hole and a climb of 6m down a ladder in water cascading over the dam wall leads into the downstream Bung Hole Series, a stream cave system about 700m long, with several interesting features. A few metres before the Bung Hole dam is a brick wall, built in the 1920s to try to maintain water levels in a drought – with little success as

water leaks through a submerged bedding plane. Immediately below the dam wall, the leaking water falls into the stream cave through a low bedding plane. Shortly downstream an arch on the right leads to the bottom of Block Hall, a high cavern in New Rake, though the vein is so poor in lead ore that the miners did not work it. It takes its name from a large limestone block some 10m up: it looks precarious from below but is firmly wedged and it is possible to climb beneath it. Using bolting techniques the cavern above has been climbed for 60m to reach a low crawl into the White River Series of Peak Cavern. Downstream from Block Hall the Bung Hole streamway continues to a point where a flat-out crawl in the stream is met, but fortunately there is a dry Short By-Pass passage on the left. Above the low section of streamway there are mine workings with much calcite and a little lead ore, and there are signs of the miners having installed a boardwalk from the dam as far as these stopes. Here the miners apparently worked upwards, but the route is now choked at the bottom of the Nameless Pitch in the White River Series. The old miners came close to reaching this series but seemingly never completed the climb. The miners also seemed to have made a bypass tunnel to the flat-out section of the streamway but it is full of collapsed debris from above, including large fallen blocks of stalagmite.

The streamway continues into the high Rift Cavern with a false floor built at its entrance for processing ore. A ladder climb of some 18m to the left up Egnaro Aven ("orange" spelt backwards from the coloured flowstone) leads to Colostomy Crawl – a tortuous "dry" but very muddy link via Liam's Way and the Trenches to Peak Cavern's Treasury Chamber. Rift Cavern ends in Puttrell's Pool where the early 20th-century explorer J.W. Puttrell thought the accessible cave ended. However, wading waist-deep into the pool reveals a low arch on the left and the streamway continues for another 400m or so – the Lower Bung Hole Series. Erosion has not yet cut much of a canyon in its floor but there is a series of cascades and submerged potholes to negotiate. There are two inlet stream passages: one soon after Puttrell's Pool emits a small stream from one of the bricked-up swallets in the Far Canal tunnel and crawls lead back to the upper Bung Hole streamway – the Long By-Pass. Further downstream is Window Passage, which also drains from openings in the Far Canal, but two short sumps have to be passed en route and the passage becomes impossibly tight near the canal, so neither of these inlets provides a through route. Near the end of the Lower Bung Hole Series a short branch on the right leads to a sump leading to a pit in the floor of the Treasury in Peak Cavern; Treasury Sump is 27m long and is passable by cave-divers only. The last section of the streamway is down a wide inclined bedding cave with little vadose entrenchment: it ends in a final downstream sump and the water resurges some 900m away at Russet Well, passing beneath the Peak Cave drainage en route. The final sump has been dived for a distance of 155m before becoming rather constricted. Both the final sump and Russet Well are

at an altitude of 187m. A branch tube down the bedding cave is Overspill Passage, also leading to a sump not far from the terminal sump in the main streamway. Most of the stream caves below the Bung Hole are subject to flooding in wet weather and water backs up to overflow via the Treasury sump in Peak Cavern, where it rises far enough to discharge via the Upper Gallery and through the Mucky Ducks and the Wallows to join the Peak Cavern stream in the Five Arches.

A notable feature of the Lower Bung Hole streamway is that it lies directly below part of Peak Cavern's Upper Gallery, with about 14m of limestone beds between them. Another part of the streamway near the Rift Cavern is directly below the White River Series.

A complete exploration of all these parts of the Speedwell's stream caves needs several days' hard work. However, a visit to the Far Canal and the stream caves beyond leading to Cliff Cavern and Main Rising can be made in a few hours and is an experience not to be missed if the opportunity arises, but climbing the high caverns is for specialist cave explorers only. Much of my early exploration in the 1940s was done in old sweaters and overalls which did not keep the cold out; neoprene wetsuits are much more comfortable today.

Much of the Speedwell cave system had been visited by the 18th-century miners in search of lead ore, leaving us with the question: was mining by means of canal tunnels and boat haulage a profitable enterprise? Unfortunately few records have survived and we do not know how much

lead ore was produced. The traditional story told by generations of cave guides is that £14,000 was invested with a yield of £3,000 worth of lead ore. If these figures are true, the enterprise was far from profitable – but where the figures come from and whether they are reliable we have no idea. The Barmaster's books contain detailed records of lead mining but the volume for the critical period is missing. Active mining lasted little more than 25 years and had more or less ceased by the late 1790s when the Speedwell Cavern became a tourist attraction, providing the rare experience of boating underground. A brief renewal of mining occurred in the 1840s.

The enterprise of lead mining by the canal tunnels was of special interest to late 18th-century industrialists and attracted early visitors. Eventually this led to redevelopment for tourists, which continues to the present day. Thus the old lead mine has become a "gold mine" for the cavern operators.

The Speedwell Cavern's stream cave is the principal drainage for the Castleton area, but with sumps at both ends it is unlikely that the system will ever be fully explored. Much of the upstream drainage system seems to be via mineral veins with cavities possibly going several tens if not hundreds of metres deep between Perryfoot, Giants Hole and the Main Rising. Similarly, at the downstream end of the Bung Hole Series the drainage is probably via bedding planes and vein cavities in the phreatic zone as yet unexplored with final resurgences at Russet Well and Slop Moll.

Two of the most important discoveries in recent years have been the vast open caverns of Leviathan and Titan. Indeed, during the exploration of Castleton's caves, information turns up in some unlikely places – in this case Cambridge University Library manuscript collections. It was there that historian Ian Ousby found the diary of a late 18th-century graduate, James Plumptre, who toured various parts of Britain with his tutor, John Dudley, in 1792–3. The diary was published by Ian Ousby in 1992 as *James Plumptre's Britain: the journals of a tourist in the 1790s*. Plumptre's hand-written diary may have been intended for publication at the end of the 18th century, but he entered the Church and it was over a century later when his papers were eventually given to Cambridge University library. His journal contained a description of his visit to the Castleton caves wherein his comments on Peak Cavern add little to what is generally known.

However, he was referred to an un-named lead mine which he toured on 24th August 1793. From his comments it was obviously the Speedwell Mine, though he did not use that name. Plumptre and his tutor, escorted by two miners, boated along both canals and then went along a boardwalk over the stream course beyond what we now know as the Whirlpool, as far as the Boulder Piles. Here a long-standing problem to modern explorers was what lay above the choked holes in the roof where piano-sized rocks were "supported" with rotten timbers. Plumpt-

re's journal gave the answer – in 1793 they had climbed up past these boulders into a vast bee-hive-shaped cavern, and thence up miners' timbers for 40 yards to where a mineral vein was being worked, evidently New Rake. The miners said that still higher there was a way out to the surface but that it was by another man's mine so they never went out that way. Plumptre and his party returned by the route they had come.

As soon as Plumptre's journal entry became known to the caving fraternity, it was realized that "the other man's mine" might have been James Hall's Over Engine Mine on New Rake, which had been explored by members of the British Speleological Association in 1963 (often shortened to JH Mine). The shaft was 48m deep and a level to the east was blocked by collapsed deads (waste rock stowed on overhead timbers). With Plumptre's comments to spur the cavers on, this blockage was cleared in the early 1990s, followed by several more collapses of waste rock. Then a hole going downwards was found: its awkward nature gave it the name Bitch Pitch. Descending it for 40m took them into a cavern which had been used by the miners for processing their ore, and various decaying pieces of equipment were lying around. Now known as the Miners' Workshop, the cavern had no fewer than fourteen openings leading off, mostly blind workings. One contained unusual green calcite crystals. Two others led into a large pit going downwards – the top of the cavern recorded by Plumpt-

re, now known as Leviathan. The rotten remains of timbers up to 6m long across the top of the cavern suggest the former presence of a platform but the size of these timbers posed a problem – how did the miners get them into the mine? Almost certainly they were brought in from the Speedwell Mine before the holes in the roof at the Boulder Piles were blocked. There were also relics of a ladder-way wedged in the walls.

Leviathan is in two parts with a slope between. A descent by abseiling rather more than Plumptre's estimated 40 yards (nearer 75m) took the cavers to a boulder floor – right on top of the chokes in the roof at Speedwell's Boulder Piles. The chokes are full of large fallen boulders and Plumptre's route remains blocked. However, digging in a hole on one side led through a choked bypass where a shaft opened out into a connection to the Speedwell streamway. It now has a fixed ladder climb and an inclined crawlway. The total depth of JH is 185m.

The entrance shaft and Bitch Pitch pass through two thin volcanic horizons: the first is at 14m depth in the entrance shaft, nearly a metre thick, whilst the second is partway down Bitch Pitch, about 40cm thick. Neither is thick enough to be considered as the Cavedale Lava, which is 20m thick at outcrop, but the volcanic horizon in the entrance shaft may be the same wayboard as in Nettle Pot.

James Hall Over Engine Mine dates from 1755, 16 years before the Speedwell project started. The connection from JH to the

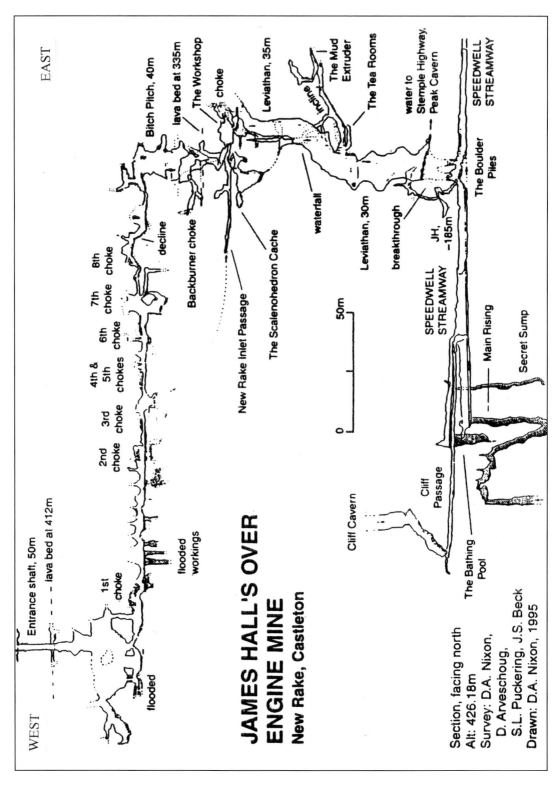

Profile of James Hall Over Engine Mine and Leviathan showing the relationship to Speedwell Cavern (by D.A. Nixon et al).

Speedwell streamway and the evidence from the separate "lost" cavern recorded by Pilkington in 1789 confirm that the late 18th-century miners knew of two routes to the stream caverns before they excavated the canal tunnels. It also demonstrated their surveying ability to plan the route and depth of the tunnels so that they met the streamway at the right place.

At the bottom of Leviathan a low passage led off to the southeast, but it was full of miners' waste washed in by the shower of water falling from high above. About 30m of hands-and-knees crawl were dug out and led to an inlet at the north-west end of Stemple Highway in Far Peak Extension, thereby solving the problem of how the miners had reached the Extension and left initials and timbers when modern access from Peak Cavern's Far Sump was by a dive 385m long. A team of explorers led by Dave Nixon could now reach Far Peak Extension without diving and they continued the investigation. A small stream inlet attracted attention: it came from a choke of massive boulders close to the inner end of Far Sump and after several attempts over a period of years a tortuous route upwards amongst these piano-sized boulders allowed the explorers to climb 35m and enter the foot of an even larger cavern than Leviathan in 1999. It was named Titan and turned out to be the highest natural cavern in Britain, with a height of 146m. It is mostly 30 to 50m wide, hourglass-shaped with a narrow section, the Event

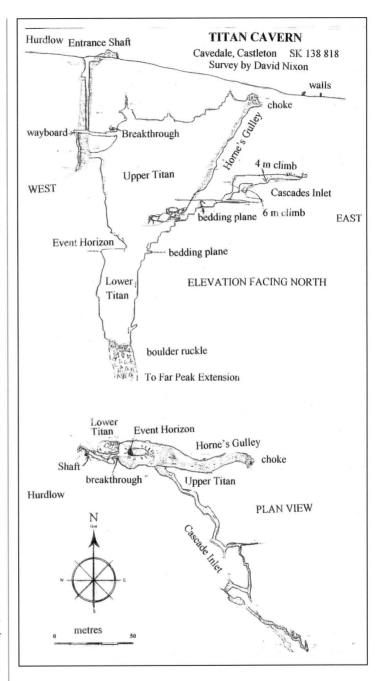

Horizon, 62m above the floor. A small stream enters from a side passage to the south-east. Higher up, towards the top Upper Titan is nearly 100m wide in places and it is a vast cathedral of a cavern. No evidence was found that the 18th-century miners had ever reached it.

Over a period of six days, Titan was climbed with the help of bolting techniques to a final height of 146m. Add on the climb up through the boulder choke and it is almost 180m high. A thin mineral vein in the roof of Titan contains a small amount of Blue John fluorspar. A small stream enters above the Event Horizon and some 200m of lateral passages lead up several cascades in a south-easterly direction. Digs through various chokes may lead to further passages.

Back in Upper Titan, a loose climb up a steep slope of boulders is Horne's Gulley; after some 120m it terminated in a choke less than 10m from the surface. Horne's Gulley sloped steeply up to the east along a mineral vein. About 15m below the top of the main Titan cavern was West Passage, a phreatic tube three metres in diameter but blocked by a choke after 10m. Digging induced subsidence in a long-abandoned lead mine shaft on the surface 50m above in 1999. Over the next three years a shaft 45m deep and 1.4m diameter was sunk from the surface on the south side of Hurdlow, close to upper Cavedale. An adit was then driven east for 20m to penetrate the choke in West Passage in May 2003, thus providing much easier access to Titan with the possibility of through trips to Far Peak Extension, Leviathan and Speedwell. Thus both JH Mine's Leviathan and Titan now provide access routes to Far Peak Extension and thence to Speedwell Cavern's streamway. Both now have steel lids for security. For those with the necessary equipment and experience this is now the deepest potholing in Britain, over 200m below the surface.

Exploration continues in a passage going west from the bottom of Titan's entrance shaft where an internal shaft 25m deep has been sunk in an attempt to reach a continuation of West Passage beyond the choke. It may reveal Titan II one day.

Both Leviathan and Titan were formed by phreatic solution guided by thin mineral veins, a category of caverns now known as Vein Cavities. Though entered from JH Mine on New Rake, Leviathan appears to be directly beneath another mine, Eyre's Grove, of which few details survive. Titan is on a thin vein south of New Rake. Other vein cavities nearby include Stemple Highway, Cliff Cavern and the Bottomless Pit in Speedwell Mine. Titan is much higher than the latter. Sinkholes (dolines) near the head of Cavedale and adjacent to New Rake suggest that other caverns just as big may lie nearby, as yet not entered by modern explorers. Digging these out might produce some surprises. Indeed if the old lead miners had sunk their shaft directly above Titan they would have got a nasty surprise when they broke through. In contrast to the partly mined JH Mine and its associated cavern Leviathan, Titan is entirely a natural cavern.

"The Early Explorers thought it a matter of Personal Honour to descend In Puris Naturalibus – they dressed for the Occasion" (cartoon from the Puttrell collection – artist unknown).

High on the northern slopes of Treak Cliff and opposite the great Mam Tor landslip, the Blue John Cavern is said to have been open to tourist visits from the 1780s, but these were probably rather few and far between at first. Until the 1830s the tour included climbing down and up a "miners' ladder" of stemples, wooden beams set into the rock in the sides of a pothole some 20m deep, not a task for the faint-hearted tourist! Around 1836 to 1840 the pothole was bypassed by blasting out a series of inclined tunnels with ramps and stone steps and visits became much easier. The switchback arrangement is still part of the tourist route.

The history of the Blue John Cavern goes back at least a century earlier. There are archival records of thirty miners working in "The Waterhole" in 1709–1710. They were ostensibly working for lead ore, and "150 tons" were recorded, though unlikely. Any galena obtained was probably from loose blocks in the sediments on the floor of the cavern as there is little trace of lead-bearing mineral veins in the walls there today; certainly not enough to keep thirty miners busy. It is likely that they were also extracting Blue John fluorspar, though the venture was short-lived and nothing is known of any ornamental craft using Blue John until 40 years later. Exactly which part of the present cavern constituted The Waterhole is also in doubt; it was also known as Waterhull and Walton's Hole, though the last was probably a mishearing as no Waltons are known to have been involved in mining there. Another interpretation of the early 18th-century comments is that in addition to the present entrance, there was a second in the wooded depression 200 metres to the east. Now blocked, the latter led into a high chamber near the Stemple Cavern, which is well off today's tourist route. From there the miners evidently found their way through most of the cave system. They appear to have reached the bottom of the Pothole by an unknown route and realized that this was below the Blue John workings near the present entrance. Apart from the latter there was an old shaft on the hilltop behind the present entrance: this has been alleged to be Roman but no archaeological evidence of the Romans working here has ever been found.

In 1765 the Barmaster's book recorded Henry Watson of Ashford-in-the-Water, near Bakewell, setting up "16 pairs of stows on Treak Cliff back for anything and what he could get". In lead-mining jargon this means that Henry Watson was mining something other than lead ore, and he was getting Blue John, which he wanted for his inlay work in his marble works at Ashford. Henry Watson was protecting his interests by ensuring that the Barmaster had his mines recorded as lead mines. The stows were wooden windlasses, effectively badges of ownership of sixteen separate mines on the rough ground of the top of Treak Cliff. Unfortunately we have no record of where these sixteen mines were but at least some may have been above the alleged Roman workings noted above. The Old Tor Mine in the Winnats Pass may have been one of the sixteen.

Another story is that in 1768 two miners, William Royse and Joseph Kyrke, requested the Barmaster to "nick" the stows as the old mine was not being worked and they could gain possession under lead-mining law. Within two years they claimed that they were the original discoverers of Blue John, but the claim seems to have been "sales talk" as Blue John had been in production at least ten years earlier and known about fifty years before. Descendants of William Royse were custodians and guides through most of the 19th century and up to World War I, when Sir Charles Markham bought the cavern and its mineral rights for private use. Later, about 1922, Arthur Ollerenshaw bought the cavern and his family have operated the cavern ever since.

With several veins of good Blue John fluorspar, the cavern was a principal source of the brightly-coloured semi-precious stone. To confuse matters it was known for a time in the late 18th century as Tre Cliff Mine, long before the tourist Treak Cliff Cavern got its name in 1935. It shared production with Henry Watson's sixteen mines on Treak Cliff Back, and with the Millers and Cliff Blue mines on the east face of Treak Cliff. The two last are now parts of Treak Cliff Cavern.

Readers are referred to the Treak Cliff Cavern chapter for a summary of the origin of Blue John fluorspar. In the Blue John Cavern the setting is slightly different as the cavern is entirely beneath the boulder bed and instead the fluorspar crystallized

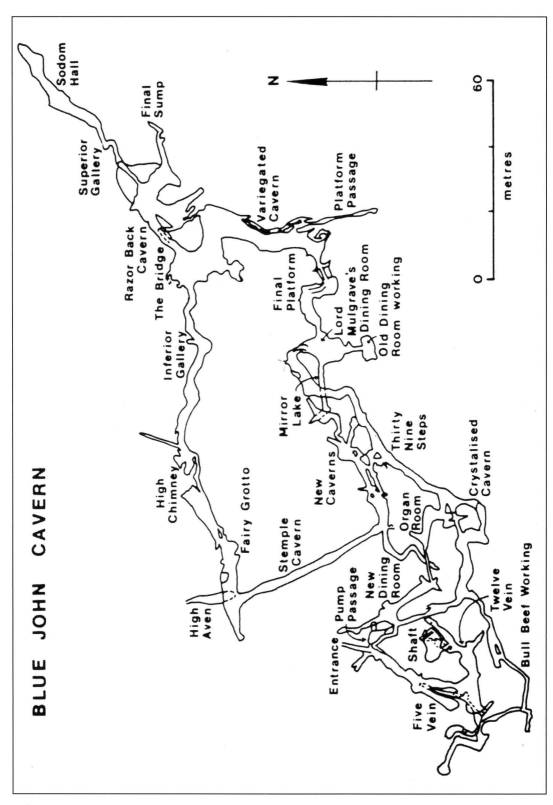

Sketch plan of the Blue John Caverns.

as linings in ancient caves dating back to mid-Carboniferous times.

The Blue John Caverns attracted some early cave explorers. At some point in Victorian times Lord Mulgrave, whose seat was at Port Mulgrave near Whitby on the Yorkshire coast, is said to have spent a week exploring with a company of miners. With no contemporary accounts available, neither the date nor how he got involved are known and what they did for a whole week is a puzzle as one can explore the whole cave system in a day! They are said to have eaten their meals in the large cavern still known as Lord Mulgrave's Dining Room. The famous late-19th-century French speleologist E.A. Martel explored the system about 1895. Ignoring protests from the guide, he climbed over the barrier in the Variegated Cavern and explored as far as the Rabbit Hole. He also went up the Inferior Gallery. Later he published a sketch profile done from memory with few actual measurements taken. The Sheffield speleologist J.W. Puttrell explored the cavern in the early 20th century: his survey was the first to show the layout in any detail: it was published in several early caving books.

The Blue John cave system appears to have been developed from two separate streams sinking into swallets. Neither is active today and the exact positions of the sinks are unknown. However, two main natural stream caverns start south and east of the entrance and unite near the bottom. These two are the show cave seen by visitors and the Inferior Gallery leading back to Stemple Cavern, which is not on the tourist route. Each swallet must have engulfed streams flowing off Mam Tor into the upper part of Odin Sitch. Forming phreatic tubes at first, the swallet streams were later well supplied with abrasive sand off Mam Tor and canyon-like vadose streamways were eroded out. A small stream still enters the lower passages from a shower falling into the Bull Beef workings. It finally disappears into an impenetrable sump at the bottom of the cave system. Dye tests have shown that the water then passes by an unknown course to reappear 1.5km away at Russet Well in Castleton: the watercourse is probably along the foot of Treak Cliff through the voids of the Boulder Beds.

The present entrance is down a flight of steps with miners' stone arching above. These lead into the First Cavern and a few yards ahead are two low branch passages into workings for Blue John stone. One of these is the Five Vein and the other is known as the Roman level, though no archaeological evidence of Roman mining has come to light. Turning sharp left the first incline down the Pothole leads down via a series of switchbacks. A short branch was used as a World War II store for Manchester University's stock of radium, though little of the laboratory equipment survives today. At the bottom of the Pothole, Ladies Walk is a comfort-

Crystalline Cavern in Blue John Caverns (P.D)

able walking-size passage with a branch into the Bull Beef vein of Blue John, so named from its purplish-red colouring. A heavy cascade of water falls into the Bull Beef workings and is culverted away under the Ladies Walk to re-appear in the Dining Room workings. Ahead is a narrow cleft known as Fat Man's Misery leading suddenly into the Crystallised Cavern.

At about 10m high and 3m wide the Crystallised Cavern is the start of the main cavern. It is named from its walls being coated with stalagmitic formations, and it was once illuminated by a ring of candles on an iron candelabrum hoisted aloft by a rope over a pulley. The main cavern is an impressive example of a vadose canyon up to 25m high and 10m wide, all eroded out by a former stream. A short branch on the left is into the former workings for the Organ Room vein of Blue John, named from a row of stalagmite columns destroyed long ago. Continuing down the main cavern there are more branches into workings for Blue John on the left, with passages leading to the Stemple Cavern. The main visitors' route then descends a staircase into Lord Mulgrave's Dining Room. This large circular chamber is reputed to be where his lordship and a party of miners rested for lunch breaks when exploring the cave system. The cavern has "inverted potholes" in the roof, characteristic of phreatic solution when the cave was still below the water table.

The Dining Room has a vein of Blue John visible at one side and a low branch passage, which contains a shallow pool known as the Mirror Lake, leads into the Old

and New Dining Room workings. A trickle of water enters here and is channelled beneath the floor to re-appear a few yards further down the route to the last cavern shown to the public – the Variegated Cavern.

The visitors' route ends on a platform across the vast Variegated Cavern. One of the largest caverns in Britain, it is some 30m high and over 100m long, though this is obscured by the bend in the middle. Visitors return from here by retracing the entry route, with the prospect of an arduous climb back to the surface.

The show cave is probably the largest vadose stream cave in Britain open to visits by the general public today. Until the 1960s visits were by "romantic" candlelight, just as the old miners must have seen it, but the installation of an electric lighting system has made the vast spaces much easier to appreciate.

For the cave explorer, a climb down from the platform in the Variegated Cavern leads to the confluence with the Inferior Gallery, which rises steeply back towards the Fairy Grotto and the Stemple Cavern, though at one point it is so tight that only thin midgets can get through. Stemple Cavern can also be reached via the Dining Room workings and a short climb up Stemple Cavern leads to the Fairy Grotto, decorated with many straw stalactites.

Beyond the barrier the route from the Variegated Cavern is partly blocked by a rock mass known as the Bridge. Beneath it the Rabbit Hole is a muddy chimney leading down to the final chamber, which is divided by a razor-back ridge. Ropes or ladders are needed to descend the

far side, where the huge cavern suddenly closes down to an impenetrable sump. The water has been dye-tested to re-appear at Russet Well. High above this last chamber, rock-climbing cavers reached the Superior Gallery rising back towards the surface. The largest chamber is Sodom Hall, liberally decorated with stalactites; no evidence was found that the miners had seen this section of the cave.

The Blue John Cavern is the source of some of the most colourful veins of Blue John fluorspar, distinguished by the pattern of colour banding – Twelve Vein, Five Vein, Old and New Dining Room Veins, New Cavern Vein, Bull Beef Vein and Organ Room Vein. Some of these, notably Bull Beef and Organ Room Veins, are worked out and there is little chance of finding any more.

The Blue John Caverns are only about 300m south of the major lead vein worked in Odin Mine, but no connection has been found, and no Blue John is known to occur in Odin Mine, though it is present in voids in the Boulder Bed very close to the mine entrance. Perhaps the Blue John deposits represent an early phase of mineralization and were already in place when the Odin fissure and vein were formed.

Thus, the Blue John Caverns leave us with several unsolved problems. Who really discovered them and when? Where exactly was the Waterhole? Where were Henry Watson's sixteen mines? What drew Lord Mulgrave to explore them? Where were the original stream inlets? Why does the large vadose canyon end so abruptly? Future research may answer some of these questions.

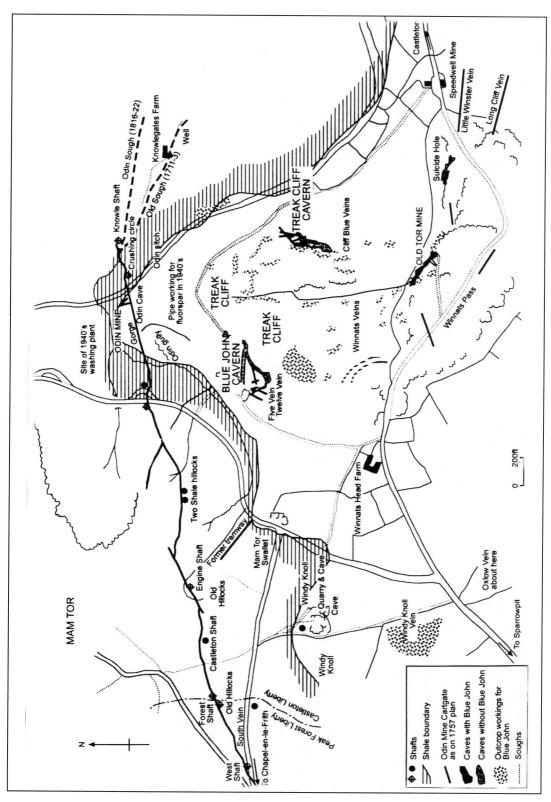

Blue John deposits and Odin Mine relationship map.

7 TREAK CLIFF CAVERN

Lying beneath the steep eastern face of Treak Cliff, this cavern is the youngest of Castleton's four show caves, having been opened to the public in 1935. It consists of two series: the outer caverns with veins of Blue John fluorspar and an inner series of stalactite grottos. The discovery of the former dates from 18th-century miners' activities, whilst the inner grottoes were discovered during Blue John mining operations in 1926. Until then the outer part of the cave system was a series of ancient caverns enlarged by mining, but of little interest to tourists. The discovery of the grottoes changed all that. It is the shortest of Castleton's show caves but it is packed with interesting and geologically diverse features.

Mining operations for Blue John on the steep eastern fore-reef face of Treak Cliff commenced in the mid-18th century,

though the exact date is unknown. At first there were two separate mines for two varieties of Blue John known as Millers and Cliff Blue Veins. Who Miller was is unknown, but his vein was in demand in the 1760s for use in a variety of ornaments and for panels inlaid in fireplaces and in churches. Millers Mine was higher up the hill and the Cliff Blue Vein was mostly in the lower workings. Sometime in the 1760s the two mines were combined underground. Unfortunately, as it was not a lead mine, the records in the lead miners' Barmaster's book give little information on mining for Blue John, but in 1769 a newspaper advertisement noted "80 tons of good spar" for sale by auction, and in the same year, Matthew Boulton of Birmingham is known to have bought 14 tons at £5-15s-6d per ton for use in his famous ormolu ornaments. A year ear-

lier he had made an unsuccessful attempt to lease or purchase all the rights to Blue John, using the pioneer geologist John Whitehurst as an intermediary to keep his name secret.

Amongst other 18th-century purchasers of Blue John in bulk were Joseph Brown & Sons, who had a marble works in Derby. There they used Blue John for both inlay work and larger ornaments such as fireplace panels. The Brown family was related to the Hall family in Castleton and it is likely that one supplied the other with Blue John. Also, from the 1740s Henry Watson operated a marble mill at Ashford-in-the-Water, near Bakewell, and he used Blue John as an inlaying material in Ashford Black Marble ornaments. The Barmaster recorded Henry Watson as having sixteen pairs of stows (windlasses) "for anything and what he could get" (i.e. anything other than lead ore) on Treak Cliff back in 1765, implying that he had that number of separate mines for Blue John, though no record of their locations survives.

Together, the auction sale, Boulton's purchase and Watson's mining interests indicate that Blue John production and its use in ornaments were well established in the 1760s. Vague references suggest that blue or "azurine" spar was known about 1700 and that mining in the nearby Waterhole Mine (now part of the Blue John Cavern) was in progress in 1709–1710, but no further details are known. Somewhere about 1750–1760 adits were driven into the hillside to reach

Mining Blue John fluorspar in Treak Cliff Cavern (P.D)

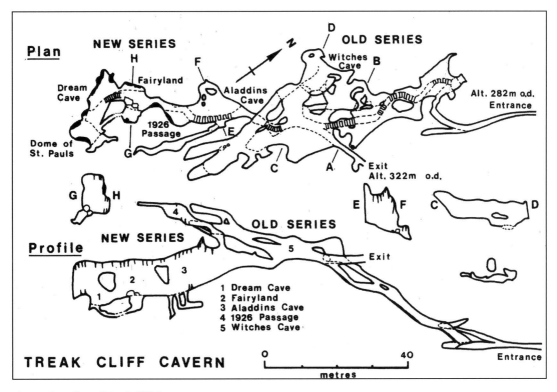

Plan and section of Treak Cliff Cavern.

the ancient caverns lined with Millers and Cliff Blue veins. These adits form the entrance and exit tunnels for today's visitors to Treak Cliff Cavern. In the late 1930s the cave was known as the Wonder Cavern and its name was spelled out in white-painted boulders on the hillside; this was a potential landmark for German bombers in World War II so it was obliterated.

The Blue John veins were deposited from hot mineralizing fluids (known as hydrothermal fluids, around 120° C) in ancient caves and in voids within the sheet of limestone boulders which blanket the outer slope of the mass of reef limestone. Geologists now recognise Treak Cliff as a complex reef system marginal to the White Peak's limestone lagoon. A profile through this arrangement of limestones can be seen in the walls of the Winnats Pass to the south of Treak Cliff. The geological story is that in the middle of the Carboniferous period, around 310 million years ago, Britain lay astride the equator and lime sediments were deposited in a tropical sea. Soon after they had hardened the area was uplifted and the top of Treak Cliff's reef was eroded off to yield the sheet of boulders now lying low down on the east face of the hill. At the same time, ancient caves were formed within the reef limestones beneath the boulders. The complex of reefs and boulders was then covered by shales heralding the Millstone Grit delta, whose sandstones now form Mam Tor and the gritstone moors and edges of the Dark Peak. The hot mineralizing fluids were introduced later when the area was under a cover of some two kilometres of Millstone Grit and Coal Measures. The fluids reacted with cooler and more oxygenated waters already present in the limestone and the result was the crystallization of fluorspar, lining the ancient caves and the voids between the boulders. The growing crystals trapped oily matter with its absorbed minute traces of uranium derived from the shales: the combination yielded the blue colouration. Radiation from the minute traces of uranium affected the crystal structure and gave rise to optical effects – the blue-purple colours. The characteristic colour banding of Blue John was caused by intermittent changes in the flow pattern through the complex plumbing system of ancient caves and voids. Rapid flow yielded uncoloured crystal layers while slow flow trapped oil with

Castleton Caves

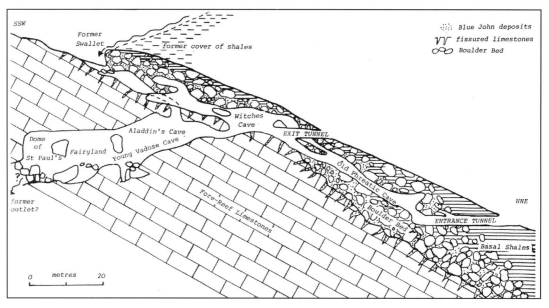

Profile to show the relationship of Treak Cliff Cavern to the Boulder Bed.

traces of uranium and gave us the blue-purple bands.

In a much more recent geological period, the Cenozoic, perhaps a million or two years ago, deep-seated solution under phreatic conditions enlarged part of the void system and resulted in the phreatic caves of the outer part of Treak Cliff Cavern. Relics of the upper half of one of the phreatic tubes can be seen in the roof of the grottoes. Gradually the whole area was uplifted and the remaining cover of Millstone Grit was slowly eroded off. Rainwater run-off from an earlier and much larger version of Mam Tor sank in a swallet above the present cavern and coursed through the Boulder Bed, re-using the ancient caves and exposing their Blue John deposits in the cave walls, whence blocks fell to accumulate on the floors. The stream off Mam Tor changed course and cut the vadose canyon-type caverns of today's grottoes, developed entirely within the fore-reef limestones behind.

How far the erosion progressed is not known as the canyon floor is hidden under fallen boulders. At some cold stage in the Ice Age fine-grained yellowish clay, derived from wind-blown rock ground to silt-size by glaciers and known as loess, was washed in down cracks and lies on the cave floor. During warmer interglacial periods seepage waters gave us the stalactites and stalagmites, some of which are still growing today. Two old stalagmites from a side alcove have been dated by the uranium-series method as 125,000 and 131,000 years BP, showing that the cave had been left high and dry by the Ipswichian interglacial, owing to the erosional lowering of the Hope Valley floor. The hydrothermal caves with their Blue John, plus the much more recent erosional caves, are what the visitors see as Treak Cliff Cavern.

The entrance tunnel to Treak Cliff Cavern passes through the lowest shales into the first cavern, Bridge Cavern, within the Boulder Bed. The cavern is said to have extended downhill to the right but was back-filled when the visitors' path was built. A short mine working for Blue John lies to the right of the Bridge. A section through a patch of fore-reef limestone gravel is visible near the upper end of the Bridge. Climbing the staircase up to the Fossil Cavern, a rock face on the right shows limestone boulders with patches of Blue John in the intervening voids. The roof of the Fossil Cavern is the underside of a single massive slab of crinoidal limestone which slid down the fore-reef slope as part of the Boulder Bed. Fossil fragments of crinoid stems are abundant – crinoids are stalked relations of starfish with long stems composed of discs of calcite and most of the fossils are lengths of stems looking rather like Polo mints. Another climb takes visitors up into the Witch's Cave, named from the shape of a shadow on the wall.

54

Several veins of Cliff Blue are visible here and mining still takes place in short side passages. Millers Vein is in a side passage. Once again the discerning eye can note that part of the cavern is in the Boulder Bed, well seen in the roof near the exit tunnel.

Descending a short staircase takes the visitor into the fore-reef limestone below the Boulder Bed. It is full of crinoid stem fragments, and the route shortly enters the first of the grottoes found in 1926, Aladdin's Cave. The miners' original entrance was via a hole high in the roof on the left, down a drop of some 12 metres, which they negotiated on a single rope by candle-light. The present-day entry passage was dug out in the 1930s. Many stalactites hang from the roof and coloured flowstone covers the walls of Aladdin's Cave. A group of stalagmites on a boulder near the bottom are the Seven Dwarves. Beyond, a short passage leads into Fairy-land, with several little "fairy grottoes" between stalactites, stalagmites and columns where they have met. On the roof there are numerous helictites, small twisted and hook-shaped stalactitic growths where the physics of crystallization have been stronger than the pull of gravity. Overhead a sheet of flowstone on the wall forms the Frozen Waterfall. The final chamber is the Dream Cave, which houses many more stalactites, where one's imagination can see many forms. One long stalactite, paired with a stalagmite below, is the Stork. With about 5 centimetres before they meet, it is estimated that it will take 1,000 years to fill the gap. On the far side of the Dream

Fairy Grotto in Treak Cliff Cavern (P.D)

Cave is the multi-coloured Dome of St Paul's. A massive rock fall on the left means that any further continuation of the cave is inaccessible.

There is no stream in Treak Cliff Cavern today and it is not subject to flooding. However, heavy rainfall leads to many drips during wet weather which are lost by percolating into the floor. Dye tests have shown that the water re-appears at Russet Well some 13 to 20 hours later. The drainage is thought to follow a route through the voids of the Boulder Bed, passing beneath the foot of the Winnats Pass and under Peak Cavern Gorge, where it merges with water from the Speedwell Cavern.

High on the east face of Treak Cliff and to the north of the cavern a low arch-like cave only extends a few metres; below it the hillside has traces of a collapsed cave and a shaft, now blocked,

led into the single chamber of **Tree Hole**, which has some minor Blue John deposits. Together these hint at the former presence of a separate shallow cave system to the north of the tourist cave.

A **Sepulchral Cave** was found above the present tourist cave during opencast fluorspar mining operations around 1921. Only a few metres long, it contained burials of several Bronze Age people. A miner crawled in and found a round object: he called back to his mates "I've found a pomegranate" but turned it over and found it was a skull – terrified, he ran off and never returned. A few years later, more opencast working for Blue John led to the discovery of a lower passage leading into the grottoes of the tourist cave about 1926. Most of the Sepulchral Cave was destroyed by later mining and the 1926 entrance passage is concealed today.

8 THE RUSHUP EDGE SWALLETS & NEARBY CAVES

Long ago designated P1, P2 to P12, the swallet caves in Rushup Vale mark the contact of the limestone massif to the south with the shales and sandstones of the Millstone Grit Series to the north. The shales flooring the Vale's north flank are largely covered by a sheet of periglacial solifluction deposits up to 8m thick, composed of sands and pebbles derived from Millstone Grit sandstones and carried down by a freeze-and-thaw sludging movement off Rushup Edge. Later, in more temperate climatic conditions, the streams draining off Rushup Edge were entrenched into the solifluction deposits and flow in shallow channels about 5 or 6m deep.

The initial P refers to Pothole, a term used in the early 20th century for any pothole or sink in the Ingleborough region of North Yorkshire and subsequently misused for Derbyshire swallet caves, none of which are potholes in the strict sense. Other claims have been made that P stands for Point of Engulfment, Point of Penetration or Possibility of a cave below! The line of swallets extends about 2.5km in a north-easterly direction from Perryfoot and all eventually drain to Speedwell Cavern and thence to Russet Well at Castleton.

Perryfoot Cave (P1) is close to a stream sink in a deep hollow immediately north of the road opposite Perryfoot Farm. In lead-mining days it was known as the Manifold Sink. The sink has been dug out via a short series of cascades to reach the adjacent cave with its dry entrance close by. This generally tight cave has a complex of narrow passages (in-cluding the Iron Maiden) extending nearly 80m to the east with a depth of 30m. It ends in a sump in a fissure some 180m north of and 30m above mine workings in Coalpithole Mine. Water from this swallet was found to cascade into a stope between No. 1 and No. 6 Shafts, but no details of the inlet passage are known. A choked sump at the bottom of the latter's mine workings engulfs the stream at roughly the same altitude as its re-appearance in Speedwell Cavern's Main Rising 4km to the east

P0 is a small sink west of Perryfoot which was dug out to reveal a cave only 30m long.

Dr Jackson's Cave was named in honour of Dr J. Wilfred Jackson, cave archaeologist and former President of the British Speleological Association. It lies immediately west of P1 and extends west via a complex series of tubes and short pitches for some 150m to a sump at a final depth of around 60m. Although they are only a few metres apart there is no way through from Perryfoot to Dr Jackson's Cave.

Sheepwash Swallet (P2) lies about 100m to the north-east of Perryfoot Cave. Its short passage takes a stream which can only be followed for about 30m. The Perryfoot and Whitelee streams were diverted here through culverts in vain attempts to prevent the water reaching the workings of Coalpithole Mine, but the miners were disappointed when they found the diverted water also found its way into the mine. A second deep culvert was said by mid-19th-century miners to turn the water into a continuation of Sheepwash Swallet, though this appears to be beyond the point reached by modern explorers.

Gautries Hole (P3) is entered from a deep tree-lined hollow some 300m further east. The stream sinks a few metres to the east but the intervening passage is impenetrable. A downstream crawl leads to some 100m of complex passages with the stream disappearing into a boulder-choke to the east. A more or less dry passage extends west and terminates in a 9m pitch into a sump chamber, where much digging and dam building failed to make progress. Adjacent to Gautries Hole a separate hollow contains **Car Pot** with a short partly choked crawl through to Gautries Hole. In spite of its proximity to Perryfoot dye tests showed that the water flows to Jack Pot (P8 – see below).

Gautries Pot (also known as Gautries Hill Pot) is an obvious open hole 7m deep on the hillside south of Perryfoot. It has a partial fill of yellow clay but in spite of digging no extensions have been found.

Coalpithole Rake is a major WNW–ESE mineral vein crossing the hillside south of Perryfoot and extending both eastwards across Perry Dale and westwards beneath the shales north of the road. Several shafts range from 72m to about 200m deep but most are now blocked or have collapsed. At the extreme western end workings are said to have been more than 100 fathoms deep. Being well-watered the miners found it necessary to pump water from the lowest workings up to the 40 fathom level (then known as the Swallow Level). No natural caverns

The Rushup Edge Swallets and Nearby Caves

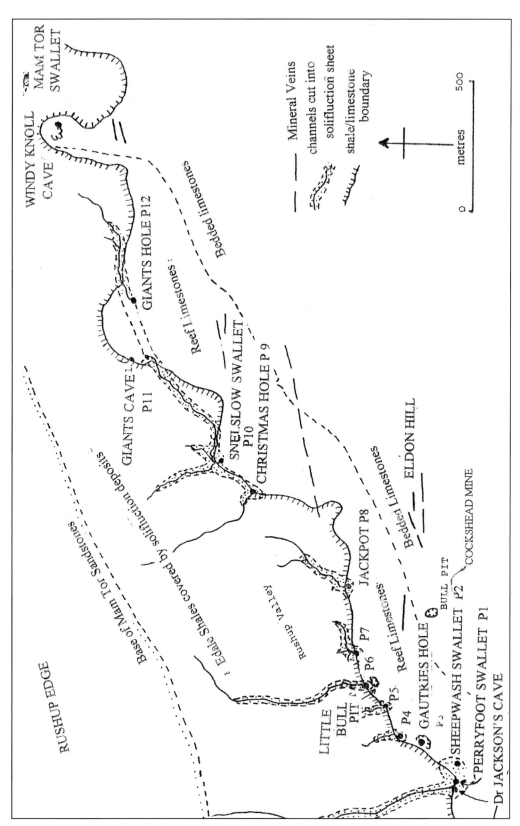

Sketch map of the Rushup Edge swallets.

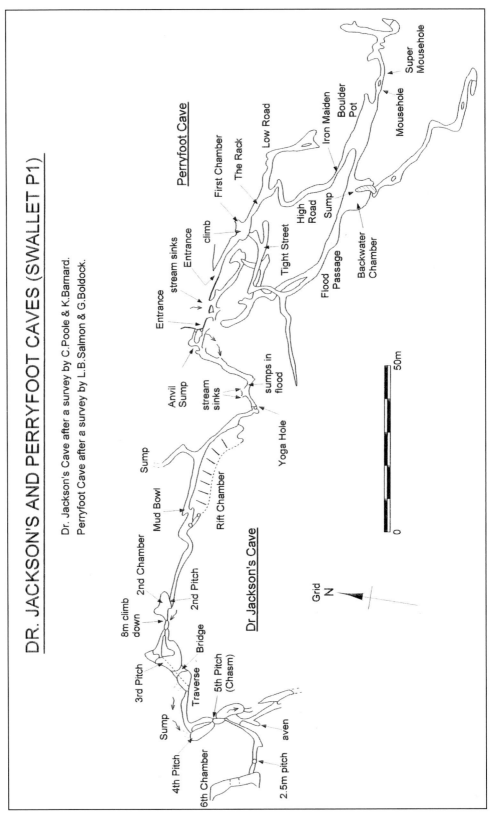

Plan of Perryfoot Cave and Dr Jackson's Hole (after surveys by L. Salmon and G. Boldock (Perryfoot) and C. Poole and K. Barnard (Dr Jackson's Cave). Courtesy of John Beck)

DR. JACKSON'S AND PERRYFOOT CAVES (SWALLET P1)

Dr. Jackson's Cave after a survey by C.Poole & K.Barnard.
Perryfoot Cave after a survey by L.B.Salmon & G.Boldock.

Perryfoot Cave

First Chamber
The Rack
Low Road
Iron Maiden
Boulder Pot
Super Mousehole
Mousehole
climb
Entrance
stream sinks
High Road
Sump
Flood Passage
Backwater Chamber
Tight Street

Entrance
Anvil Sump
stream sinks
sumps in flood
Yoga Hole

Sump
Mud Bowl
Rift Chamber

8m climb down
2nd Chamber
2nd Pitch
3rd Pitch
Traverse
Bridge
5th Pitch (Chasm)
Sump
4th Pitch
6th Chamber
aven
2.5m pitch

Dr Jackson's Cave

Grid N

0 — 50m

were recorded but the streams from the swallets around Perryfoot meet in the 40 fathom level (40 fathoms or 72m measured below the top of No. 1 shaft by the Mine Cottage in Perry Dale) and flow into a swallow to re-appear at Speedwell Cavern's Main Rising some 4km to the east. The swallow where the water is last seen was west of No. 1 shaft, beneath the slopes of Gautries Hill. It was found to be concealed by mine debris by explorers in the 1960s. The sink is variously recorded as 800 feet O.D., at 850 feet O.D. or as 870 feet O.D. but the 40 fathom level appears to be about 830 feet (246m) O.D. This is close to the altitude of the Main Rising in Speedwell but the debris blockage may mean that the true swallow is slightly lower and a completely submerged course can be inferred with water flowing through vein cavities in Watts Grove Vein and crossing into New Rake further east. When the mines were active the water resurging at Russet Well was often turbid. Dye tests have confirmed the link.

Gautries Rake is sub-parallel to Coalpithole Rake and lies some 250 to 300 metres to the south. It probably drains to the swallow in Coalpithole but no details are known.

Sludge Pit (P4) is a short cave about 100m north-east of Gautries Hole, where much sludge has been dug out with little progress. The unnamed **P5** lies about 100m further east and again has failed to yield to digging. Water from both P4 and P5 enters Jack Pot from sump B.

Little Bull Pit (P6) has a stream sinking in a walking-size cave choked with silt just a few metres in. In spite of repeated attempts at digging through the choke it has not been penetrated. A pothole above is 10m deep and has also failed to yield to much digging.

The water sinking at P6 reappears from a sump in Jack Pot.

P7 is a swallet where a moderate stream sinks about 140m north-east of Little Bull Pit. Again, much digging has failed to make progress. The stream reappears in P8 from a sump halfway down the system.

Bull Pit is not a swallet. It is a large hollow some 50m wide just north of the road, and possibly above the unknown cave system south of Little Bull Pit. With walls some 30m deep on three sides, it looks like a major collapse into an unknown cave which could be a continuation of the P6 swallet. The old lead miners are said to have sunk a shaft in Bull Pit but no workings have been found. Cavers have sunk several shafts among the boulders on the floor but no cave system has been reached.

Cockshead Mine (also known as SP pot) is a series of mine workings and caverns on the east–west Eldon Bent Vein, which continues as Perryfoot Rake, just south of the road, opposite Bull Pit. The shaft lay some 30m south-west of the gate but is now concealed. Explorations by Bernard Chandler and others in 1952–3 found the shaft to be 50m deep with mine work-

Old Man's Rift (A.C.W)

ings and cave passages to east and west, and internal shafts going at least 20m deeper. At the western end there was a substantial cavern on a cross joint trending north–south. Water levels were found to fluctuate by at least 10m but no other details of drainage were recorded. The lowest water level was still higher than the swallow in Coalpithole Mine. Some 200m to the west Red Rose Mine also went down to water. There has been no access for many years.

Jack Pot (P8) is a swallet cave which has yielded to digging. Although a very tight squeeze permits access for thin people along a bedding cave above the stream sink, the latter is the usual entrance, though sometimes waterlogged. Inside, a small vadose canyon with tight bedding crawls above (the Flats) leads via Idiot's Leap, an awkward 2m drop, and thence shortly to the First Pitch (8m). The streamway soon reaches the Second Pitch (8m) where it soon sinks in the floor of a complex of several passages, soon reappearing to flow into the Main Stream Sump (Sump 1). Above is the NW–SE Old Man's Rift, a vein cavity where it is thought that the old lead miners had been in and tested a few scrin veins; their access route was probably via shafts on the hillside above, now run-in, where there was a Speedwell Mine (no known connection with the other Speedwell at Castleton). Various climbs go up into caverns such as Mud Hall, Christmas Aven and Sand Passage but little progress has been made in spite of much digging. Separate small streams enter from Sumps D and B in short north-westerly passages below the Second Pitch, with the water coming from

nearby swallets. For non-diving cavers the system ends at Sump 1. However, cave-divers passed this after 32m and a long sinuous passage with eight more sumps has been explored, with the stream disappearing into a side branch at Sump 6 roughly on the line of Eldon Bent Vein. The water probably flows through vein cavities beneath Eldon Hill and eventually re-appears at Main Rising in Speedwell Cavern. Jack Pot totals just over 1,000m of passage to Old Man's Rift though it is less than 200m from the entrance in a straight line. There are at least 600m more passages beyond Sump 9 extending to south of the road outside Eldon Hill quarry. The complicated array of passages may reflect the cave's evolution from undulating bedding planes as the stream passed through the irregular belt of reefs into the more regular bedded massif limestones.

Christmas Swallet (P9) lies to the east of Jack Pot. A small stream follows a series of tight rifts and short passages down five pitches of 8, 10, 11, 9 and 9 metres to a sump which has been explored to a blockage at a depth of 9m. The total length is 339m and the depth 70m.

Christmas Hole lies nearer the road. A rift was dug out but later back-filled.

Snelslow Swallet (P10) is a series of narrow fissures, once taking a stream though this was diverted to Christmas Swallet during digging operations. A shaft sunk from the surface was followed by much awkward digging and reached a final depth of 57m.

Cove Hole in the nearby dry valley is a series of tight fissures dug out to a final depth of 28m.

Giants Cave (P11) (also known as Peakshill Cave) lies at the western end of a limestone reef mass known as Peakshill, lying to the north of Giants Hole. The cave is accessible in three places, the sink (sometimes designated P13), the middle cave and the resurgence. The sink is about 5m deep and leads to a low crawl which soon becomes too tight. The middle section is a single chamber reached from an obvious entrance at the western end of the reef limestone mass; the stream flows south across the chamber and disappears into a sump. It resurges from a low arch by the path to Giants Hole, where it is possible to crawl in for a few metres. The emergent stream remains on the surface and flows past the Giants Hole car park to Snelslow Swallet (P10).

Peakshill Sough is marked by a line of miners' waste hillocks north-west of Peakshill, which show that the miners drove a sough northwards under the shales as far as the road along Rushup Edge in an unsuccessful attempt to find the westerly continuation of Odin Rake; the sough tail has not been located but it may well drain into Peakshill Cave.

Giants Hole is P12 and is the subject of a separate chapter.

Eldon Hill Quarry fissures. Apart from the active swallets along the present limestone/shale boundary, it is logical to expect an earlier generation of sinks having been along this boundary before the shale cover had been eroded back to its present position. Such caves might be expected on the slopes of the limestones some hundreds of metres south of the present limestone/shale bound-

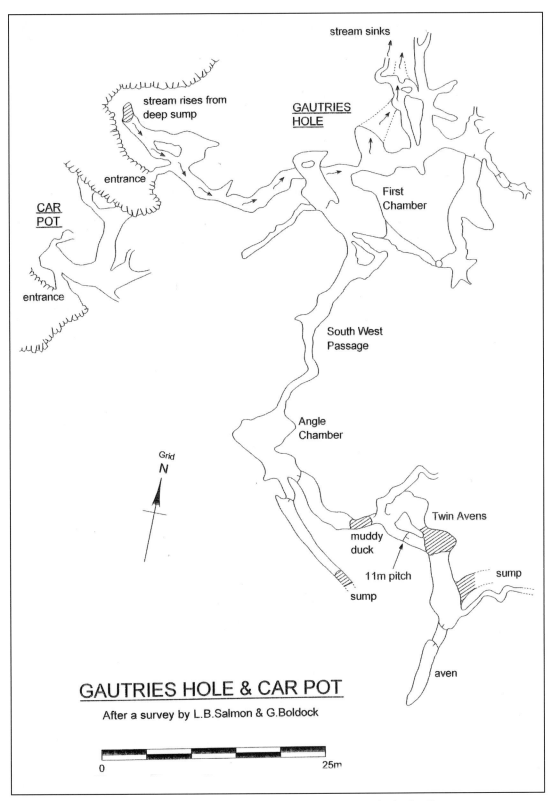

Plan of Gautries Hole (after a survey by L. Salmon and G. Boldock. Courtesy of John Beck).

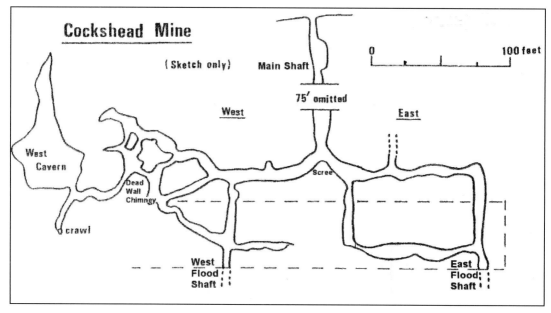

Sketch section of Cockshead Mine and caverns on Perryfoot Rake (by B. Chandler c.1953, courtesy of Paul Chandler).

ary, but little evidence of any has been found. The best known ancient caves include the group of sand, silt and clay-filled fissures found in Eldon Hill quarry. These suggest that streams flowing off Rushup Edge at a much higher level took solifluction sediments into an earlier generation of swallets abandoned subsequently. Palaeomagnetic determinations suggest that the fills may be as much as 900,000 years old, i.e. early Pleistocene. The sediment-filled passages probably extend beneath Eldon Hill, but digging any out might take many years. Eldon Hill quarry has removed several other fissure caves during its working life, some well decorated with stalactites and flowstone, and one quarry face near the entrance still bears evidence of a flowstone

sheet. Details were not recorded, and little trace remains today. An open pothole was found in the quarry floor at the eastern end but it was allegedly partly back-filled and covered with an iron plate before any caver could examine it. Two dolines in the adjacent field suggest the presence of other potholes or collapsed caverns.

Sidetrack Cave is on a bench in the eastern wall of Eldon Hill quarry and extends eastwards under the rough road to Old Moor. A crawl leads to a continuation of the former **Alsop's Cave** which was removed by quarrying. Nothing is known of the original entrance which must have been quarried away. It is likely to have been an early swallet system before the development of the present swallets. The main pas-

sage is mostly walking or stooping size of some 200m of phreatic tube with the vadose trench obliterated by sediment infill. There are fine stalactites, curtains, gour pools and cave pearls. The downstream (eastern) end is a choke. It is tempting to speculate that the cave may continue beyond the latter, possibly to an as yet unknown vein cavity. Indeed this "fossil" cave might even go as far as the White River Series in Peak Cavern.

The southern end of Eldon Hill quarry is crossed by Windle and Rush vein, marked by the **Slitherstones Mines** immediately east of the old road. Whilst no caverns are known the mine is of interest as it is said to go to 110 fathoms depth (c.200m), which would certainly be close to the water table.

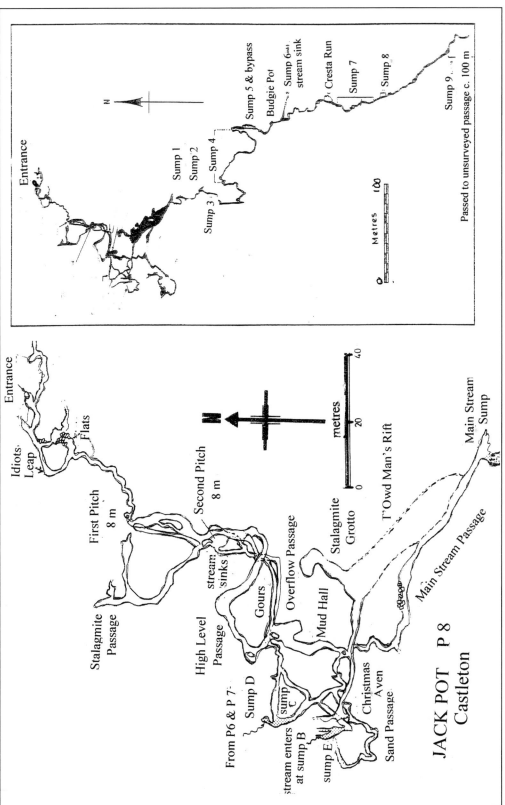

Plan of Jack Pot (P8) (after surveys by the Eldon Pothole Club with an inset of various diving surveys through sumps 1 to 9. Courtesy of D. Gill and J. Beck).

9 GIANTS HOLE

Giants Hole (P 12) is the longest and deepest of the Rushup Edge swallets near the limestone/shale margin. It has an open natural entrance taking a stream into a comfortable walking-sized passage. How it ever got the name Giants Hole is a mystery as the cave as known up to the 1950s was neither large nor extensive, being accessible for little more than 200 metres, and that with some difficulty. The entrance lies along an inclined fault plane but this is soon lost as the streamway meanders about. Not far in some high-level passages in the roof lead back to a blocked former swallet on the hillside as well as inwards to a gravel-choked passage. About 100 m into the cave the roof once lowered at the Curtain to within 30 cm of the floor where a flat-out crawl of 2 m or so lying in the stream was necessary to go any further. After a few more metres the stream flowed into a sump, too constricted for diving. Nearby a body-tight crawl high in the left-hand wall led into Pillar Chamber, with a substantial stalactite pillar on one side, long since removed by vandals. A sloping passage continued to Backwash Sump, where, after several attempts, a constricted dive of some 10 m was found to rise into a continuation of the stream cave at what came to be known as Base Camp Chamber. Bailing water out of the sump for several hours into a series of dams gave access for non-diving cavers and exploration could continue. Above Base Camp Chamber the stream re-

appeared from the downstream end of the constricted sump cascading from a tight cleft and crossing a gravel floor to the long-awaited extension of the cave, now known to include about 3 kilometres of cave passages.

A few years after this discovery the farmer made an abortive attempt to turn Giants Hole into a tourist cave. The Curtain and Pillar Crawl were blasted open to walking size and the roof of Backwash Sump removed to allow easy access to Base Camp Chamber. The stream down the entrance passage was culverted through pipes, a concrete path was laid on top and lighting installed, but floods soon ripped up the path and few tourists arrived, so it was left to the cavers.

A few metres downstream from Base Camp Chamber a series of well-decorated grottoes rise into the roof, with stalactitic layers covering coarse gravel beds containing pebbles of Millstone Grit sandstone derived from Rushup Edge, marking the downstream end of the gravel-choked passages above the entrance series. These must have been choked when the run-off from the solifluction sheet was active and the present streamway was also blocked. Soon afterwards the next obstacle appears – Garlands Pot with a drop of 7 m, usually passed with the aid of a rope or wire ladder. Prominent chert bands in the limestone have restricted erosion by the stream and form the lip of the waterfall.

At Garlands Pot the stream cascades into a small round

chamber and flows out down a high but narrow slot. Beyond, the stream course continues for over 1000 m in a narrow meandering canyon up to 20 m high. The first 600 m require squeezing through sideways, hence the name Giants Crabwalk. Well-built cavers find some sections distinctly uncomfortable, particularly the Vice. At its lower end the Crabwalk widens out at Great Relief Passage which leads down to a complex of several branch passages and sumps. The incision of the vadose canyon ends here, and beyond there are only phreatic features. A climb of some 20 m down Geology Pot or a crawl through the former St Valentine's Sump and a descent of the Filthy Five Pitches, eventually lead to a flooded vein cavity with a NW-SE trend. The fracture in the East Canal has minimal mineralization and the final chamber is 40 m high with water 25 m deep (65 m total). The Giants Hole stream disappears in the East Canal at a depth of 140 m below the surface. Surveying later established that the altitude of the water-surface to be about 245 m O.D. (c. 800 ft O.D.), close to if not identical with the Main Rising in Speedwell Cavern about a kilometre away: dye-tests have proved the hydrological connection. The coincidence of altitudes suggests that the intervening cave system is completely submerged but diving has made only limited progress from each end. The dye-tests have also demonstrated that some of Giants Hole water emerges at Whirlpool Rising. Deep drainage via mineral

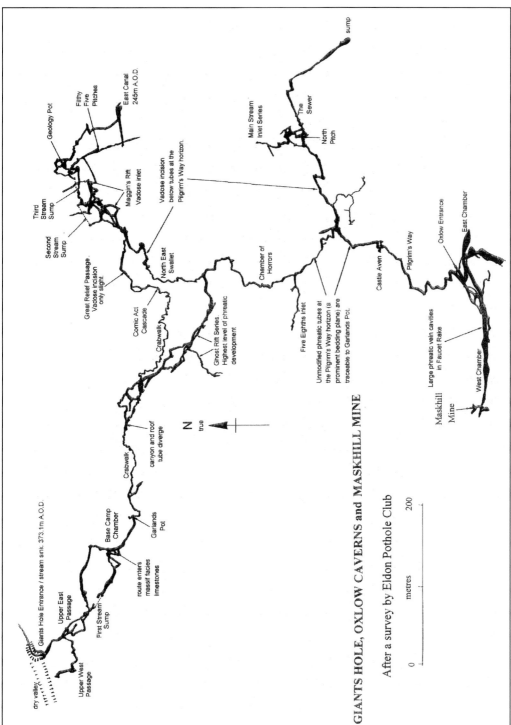

Plan of Giants Hole, Oxlow Caverns and Maskill Mine (after a survey by Eldon Pothole Club. Courtesy of John Beck).

GIANTS HOLE, OXLOW CAVERNS and MASKHILL MINE

After a survey by Eldon Pothole Club

vein cavities is the likely link, probably too tight or too deep for cave divers ever to penetrate. As discussed elsewhere in this book, the submerged system has peculiarities resulting in ebbing-and-flowing phenomena at both of Speedwell Cavern's Whirlpool and Main Risings under mild flood conditions.

From the bottom end of the Crabwalk a climb up Maginn's

Great Relief Passage at the bottom of the Crabwalk (P.D)

longer, and the descent into the Crabwalk needs care. The final descent from Great Relief Passage to the East Canal requires at least another hour each way.

The evolution of Giants Hole involves phreatic enlargement of fractures with minimal mineralization, followed by development of a tube network along bedding partings in the limestones. The first section of the cave was developed through the belt of reef limestones, accounting for the irregular passage profile at the Curtain and first sump. The cave passes from reef limestones into more regular limestone beds near Garlands Pot. One of the phreatic tubes was later enlarged by canyon incision as an acidic stream draining the south side of Rushup Edge enhanced solution of the limestone and the abrasive sand it brought in incised the Crabwalk vadose canyon. As noted above the drainage now sinks in the East Canal and goes on to Speedwell Cavern and thence to the resurgence at Russet Well. Meltwater from snow on Rushup Edge still provides enough run-off and sand to erode the floor of the canyon and this sediment eventually reaches Speedwell Cavern, and yields turbid water at Russet Well.

Uranium series dates on flowstone from various locations in Giants Hole range from 125 000 years Before Present (Ipswichian Interglacial), to 48 000-54 000 years BP (mid-Devensian interstadial) and around 3000 years BP (Holocene). These dates show that much of Giants Hole had been drained by the Ipswichian Interglacial and was in the vadose zone by about 120 000 years ago.

Rift, a NW-SE cavern 25 m high, leads to a high-level series of passages including Northeast Passage and Ghost Rift, all long abandoned by the stream. With several low meandering crawls these lead back to the roof of the Crabwalk not far below Garlands Pot, with a drop of 20 m into the streamway. Returning via this route provides a loop tour for parties of cavers, but it is not an enterprise to be taken lightly by novices.

A series of phreatic tubes branching off this high-level series of crawls leads south via Poached Egg Passage to the Chamber of Horrors and Pilgrim's Way eventually leading to New Oxlow Caverns, but it is a long tortuous passage and very low in places. With a minor inlet it is liable to occasional flood-ing so it is not an easy route to take. A branch to the east leads to North Pitch and to yet another sump.

Giants Hole totals some 3 km of passages to a depth of 140 metres. With the extended cave system first explored in the 1960s, it is much visited by caving parties. The easiest trip is a simple underground hike to Garlands Pot and back, taking less than an hour; with care and Wellington boots you need not get your feet wet! A longer trip is a descent of Garlands Pot and the sideways squeeze down the Crabwalk, awkward and tight in places. The return up the same route is hard work shuffling and squeezing uphill. At least two hours should be allowed each way. The return route through the high-level crawlways takes

Being on the crest of the apparent watershed between the Rushup and Hope Valleys, Windy Knoll Cave can only have been an active swallet before the evolution of those two valleys to their present depth. Such an ancient swallet could have taken water off the southern slopes of a former larger version of Mam Tor and the east end of Rushup Edge. The cave was breached by mid 19th century quarrying of a reef limestone knoll. The cave lies some 200 m south of the Chapel-en-le-Frith road close to the limestone/shale margin, with a roof composed of the Boulder Bed, of which a small part collapsed recently. The quarry is well-known for its palaeokarstic features such as Neptunean dykes which are fissures filled with boulders in a matrix partly composed of the overlying shales. Also there are the unique elaterite deposits, a mixture of tarry hydrocarbons (bitumens) oozing out of both boulder bed and the immediately underlying reef limestone. The bitumens are possibly the residue of an oil accumulaton in late Carboniferous times from which the lighter fractions have long since been lost by oxidation and evaporation into the atmosphere.

The cave is effectively a single chamber about 20 m long. It has a boulder slope at the entrance and fissures choked with rocks at the back. Digging amongst these has revealed a few metres of crawl-sized passage; at the end one dig led to a subsidence from the surface above. Where the drainage went when the cave was an active swallet is unknown but it probably went to Speedwell Cavern.

The cave attracted the attention of late 19th century bone hunters, particularly the Castleton antiquarian Rooke Pennington and Professor W. Boyd Dawkins of Owens College (later Manchester University). The contemporary accounts in the 1870s are illustrated only with very crude sketches of a cave plan and a section with little to relate one to the other. However, the section was said by the late Dr J.W.Jackson (once an assistant to Professor Dawkins) to refer to a separate excavation in a shallow hollow immediately outside the present cave entrance, which was back-filled after the dig. Professor Dawkins thought that a northerly contin-

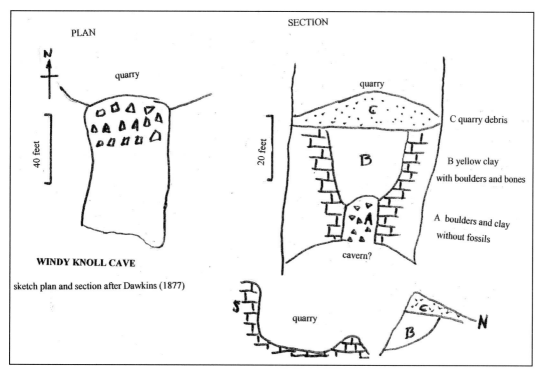

Sketch plan and section of Windy Knoll Cave (after Dawkins 1877).

Windy Knoll Cave

uation of the cave beneath both entrance slope and fissure was possible but it was not proved. The "fissure" yielded 6000 bones of deer, bison, oxen, reindeer, woolly rhinoceros, wolf, fox, bear and other late Pleistocene animals, but no human remains. The finds are preserved in Manchester, Bolton, Sheffield and Buxton Museums. Re-excavation of the fissure might yield more information.

Between the cave and the road are the remains of two old lead mine shafts, both choked and any workings below are inaccessible. The two shafts may be on a mineral vein shown on 18th century plans to be branching out of the western part of Odin Mine, which was worked beneath the shales under the fields and car park north of the road: however few details of these mine workings are known. Also there is said to be a Windy Knoll vein of Blue John but no mine workings for this variety are known today.

11 MAM TOR SWALLET

This active swallet takes a small stream off the southern slope of Mam Tor. The sink is in a hollow immediately north of the road junction. Digging has revealed a short series of chambers lying more or less on top of one another with tight passages and short climbs between. The total depth is about 10 m and the length 24 m. The water has long been thought to go to the Blue John Cavern, but dye-tests suggest it goes to Odin Mine.

This ancient lead mine, sometimes recorded as Gank Mouth, follows a series of closely parallel veins with a generally east-west trend under the southern slopes of Mam Tor. The accessible part includes the ancient open-cut near the entrance and about 300 m of mine workings along a major mineral vein steeply inclined to the north. The vein cuts across the northernmost tip of the limestone outcrop for around 200 m but the rest of the 1.5 km of workings are beneath the shale cover. It is often regarded as a single fracture but 18th century plans show that there is a series of sub-parallel en echelon factures. Mining is known to have taken place in the 17th century but probably dates back to Roman times. The mine workings were recorded on late 18th century mine plans, which show the lowest workings being some 80 m below the road outside. Drainage soughs took water away by two early 18th century soughs discharging close to Knowlegates Farm, and later in the 1820s via a long sough to an outfall close to Tricket Bridge in Castleton village.

Of the part accessible today, there is little evidence of natural caverns or of drainage to the soughs. However, the old plans are intriguing in that they record *"ye swine hole, a self-open not cut, from whence at a flood cometh a great quantity of water"*. The term "self-open" suggests the presence of a natural cavern, perhaps some sort of pipe vein or vein cavity, which was liable to flooding. The Swine Hole (Swim Hole in some accounts) was situated quite close to but much deeper than the Blue John Cavern, at the Cartgate Level roughly equivalent to the road outside Odin Mine's entrance. The source of such flood water is unknown. As far as is known all today's discharge goes to the deep Odin (Trickett) Sough.

Odin Cave lies immediately south of the mine entrance. Apparently once known as Gank Hole, it is a single natural cavern with much yellowish clay probably derived from the former cover of periglacial loess. Two other mines on the hillside above also go into small caverns with much yellow clay: all three are possibly part of an ancient cave system filled with inwashed loess.

Odin Sitch is a stream which flows from below the road junction past the Blue John Cavern entrance. It once flowed down the now dry Odin Gulley and directly across the vein and mine workings near the entrance. The stream was diverted down an 18th century leat by-passing both gulley and gorge. Today this stream flows down the valley to join Peaks Hole Water close to Castleton car park.

CAVES IN THE WINNATS PASS **13**

Suicide Cave is the best known and said to be named after a young couple who took their own lives there though no record of this has been located. It is situated low down in the north wall of the Pass and looks as if it might have been a resurgence once. The First Chamber ends with a massive boulder slope with a 5 m drop into the Second Chamber. The latter leads to a high narrow canyon passage and a climb terminates in a small chamber with any further continuation choked. The whole cave is only about 40 m long.

Buttress Hole is an obvious round hole in a limestone buttress high on the north wall of the Pass. It leads to a single round chamber with a crawl to one side.

Old Tor Mine is the largest of several workings for Blue John fluorspar. High on the north side of the Pass it is now gated for safety. The adit leads into a series of small caverns with Blue John veins in their walls. The veins are mostly exhausted now but appear to have been linings of ancient caves in the reef limestones. A steep slope leads downwards to partly flooded workings. A former open-pit working is on the cliff top above the adit with a connecting shaft concreted for safety. Another old mine has been blocked on the cliff top. A mine adit close to the road followed a thin scrin with yellow fluorspar but it does not connect with any workings for Blue John.

Several small caves on the south wall of the Pass soon end in chokes. One leads into a chimney-like cave behind Shining Tor. A spring some three-quarters of the way up the pass emits a small stream which sinks at the Windy Bend and it is probably the stream in the Assault Course Series of Speedwell Cavern. There are traces of old mine workings just above the Windy Bend on the south side of the road. Nothing is known of their extent.

Winnats Head Cave has a partly collapsed entrance in the old quarry at the top of the Winnats Pass, and the squeeze was not passed until 1976, when a series of caverns about 200 m long and 170 m deep was entered for the first time. A second squeeze led into the Main Chamber some 40 m across and floored with a mass of unstable boulders. The First Pitch was a shaft of 21 m down through these into Cornwall Avenue, a rift passage with an east-west trend. The steep boulder slope opened up into the large Fox Chamber, a vein cavity 46 m long, 15 m wide and 20 m high. There are traces of mineralization including a fluorite flat in the wall of Fox Chamber. This has a Second Pitch of 15 m in its floor, and scrambles lead down to a sump. A traverse along a shelf on the north side

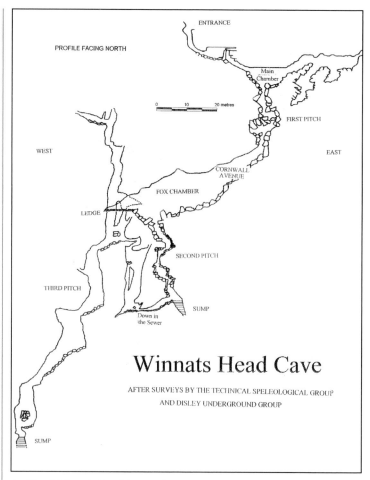

Profile of Winnats Head Cave (after surveys by the Technical Speleological Group and Disley Underground Group. Courtesy of John Beck).

of Fox Chamber leads to a crawl into a parallel rift, rising towards the surface west of the entrance. Below is the Third Pitch into a series of rifts to a terminal sump at a depth of 136 m.

Winnats Head Cave was an unexpected rift cave system whose relationship to the rest of the Castleton cave system is uncertain. A thin mineral vein crossing the cave may be an extension of a vein across the Pass further

downhill. The source of the small stream is not known but dye tests have shown that the water re-appears at the Whirlpool Rising in Speedwell Cavern.

Uranium series dates of flowstone in the upper chambers ranged from 176 000 to 191 000 years BP indicative of the Ipswichian interglacial. A sample in the lower Fox Chamber was 54 000 years old, i.e. mid-Devensian.

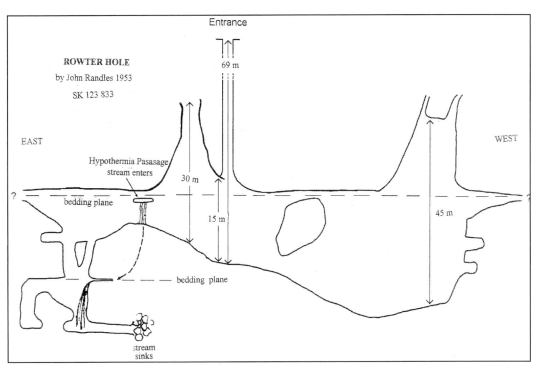

ROWTER HOLE
by John Randles 1953
SK 123 833

Entrance
69 m

EAST

WEST

Hypothermia Pasasage
stream enters

30 m

?
bedding plane

15 m

45 m

bedding plane

stream
sinks

Profile of Rowter Hole (after John Randles).

Rowter Hole is an old lead mine 244 m northeast of Rowter Farm, on the junction of Faucet Rake and the branch vein known as Slack Hole Scrin. The term "shack" or "slack" was lead miners' jargon for a "self-open", i.e. a natural cavern, so its use here indicates that the lead miners knew there were caverns in these veins. The shaft is partly ginged with miners' stonework. It is 69 m deep and at 52 m it opens out into a large cavern 18 m high, 6 m wide and 30 m long, one of the series of vein cavities in Faucet Rake. A prominent bedding plane forms the roof to most of the caverns. To the west a slope descends to the foot of the Main Chamber, with short mine workings off, whilst to the east a climb up a scree slope leads to a bedding plane which emits a small stream. Hypothermia Passage was dug out for 24 m with the water entering from a choke. In the floor of the East Chamber two short shafts (8 m each) lead to a gravel-floored bedding plane where the stream sinks.

The lowest point in Rowter Hole is at a depth of 82 m. In plan view it is near to but roughly 100 m above the final chamber in the Assault Course Series of Speedwell Cavern but no connection has been established.

15 LONGCLIFFE MINE AND POT

Roughly in the centre of Longcliffe, the steeply sloping hillside south of Speedwell Mine, in a prominent waste hillock, a short ginged shaft soon opened into the roof of a natural pothole, situated on the junction of the NW-SE Longcliffe Vein and a westerly branch vein, Slack Hole Scrin rising steeply up the hillside. In wet weather water runs from the latter vein and cascades down the pot. The shaft-cum-pot was about 40 m deep when first explored in the 1940s but the ginged section has collapsed, and the debris now blocks access to the workings at the bottom. These mine workings and small chambers extended some 60 m to the east. The system is roughly above the unexplored eastern Halfway House workings in Speedwell Mine.

The eastern end of Longcliffe Vein crosses the foot of Cowlow Nick, with several parallel WSW-ENE scrins higher up. A waste mound at the bottom of the Nick appears to have been the entrance to an adit driven southwards and this may be "The Levy" referred to in 18th century mine records. If so, it may have been the access route into mine workings and possibly caverns above the inaccessible eastern workings in Longcliffe Vein in Speedwell Mine. Even more speculative is the possibility that these led down into the hypothetical stream cave between the Bottomless Pit and Russet Well.

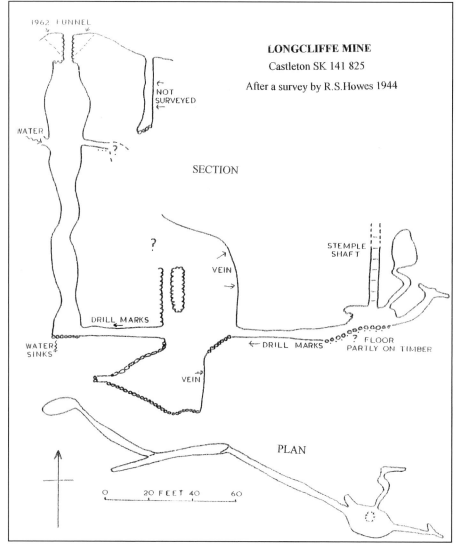

LONGCLIFFE MINE

Castleton SK 141 825

After a survey by R.S.Howes 1944

Plan and section of Longcliffe Mine and Cavern (after a survey by R.S. Howes).

1962 FUNNEL

NOT SURVEYED

WATER

SECTION

?

?

STEMPLE SHAFT

VEIN

DRILL MARKS

WATER SINKS

← DRILL MARKS

? FLOOR PARTLY ON TIMBER

VEIN

PLAN

0   20 FEET 40   60

The only natural open pothole in the Peak District, Eldon Hole is a gash 34 m long by 6 m wide on the southern slopes of Eldon Hill. Such an open abyss attracted attention from early times and there are legends of a man being lowered down in Elizabethan times but returning to the surface raving mad and dying soon afterwards. A goose is said to have been thrown down and emerged from Peak Cavern with its feathers singed

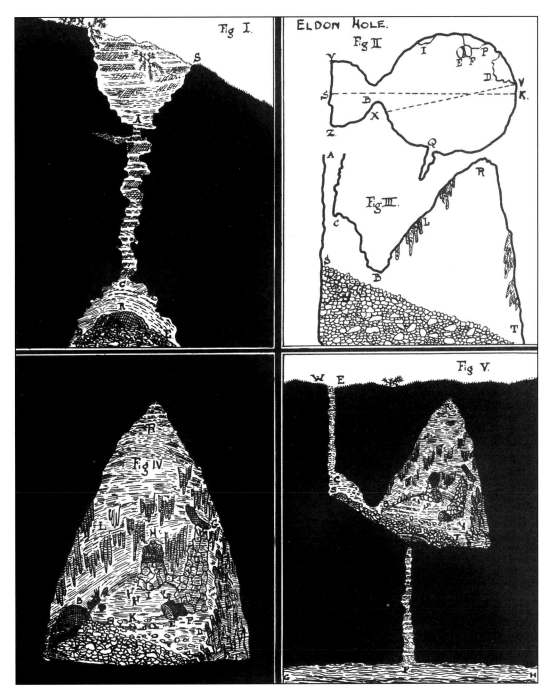

J. Lloyd's diagrams of Eldon Hole, 1777.

off by the fires of Hell! Charles Cotton, friend of the angler Isaac Walton, is supposed to have let a rope down for 884 yards (half a mile), but this may be just a fishy story.

The first factual account is that of J. Lloyd whose account in the *Philosophical Transactions of the Royal Society* in 1780 included reasonable diagrams which amount to one of the first cave surveys ever published and probably the only cave survey to appear in that scientific periodical. Lloyd showed the main pothole to be about 200 feet (60 m) deep with a low passage off to a large cavern to the east, and a further drop in its floor to a cave with a river in it.

For many years the animals were precluded from falling down the pothole by a dry stone wall, but this had to be rebuilt at intervals owing to passers by throwing rocks down. It was replaced by a wire fence which does not make a satis-

factory noise when cast into the abyss. The accumulation of walling stone at the bottom has reduced the depth to 180 feet (55 m) and the low arch is now a short timbered shaft and a crawl. In severe winters snow sometimes blocks these.

Early 20th century descents were by a bosun's chair lowered via a pulley arrangement but today's descents are either by a steep scramble down the north end (30 m) followed by a 40 m ladder pitch from a sloping ledge, or by a free-hanging ladder of 55 m from the south end.

The inner chamber is about 27 m high on a NNW-SSE fracture parallel with the main hole. It is floored by boulders with a slope to the final depth of 82 m. The walls are well-decorated by flowstone. A short branch passage on the left (north) soon closes down, though there are tales of smoke from blasting in Eldon quarry coming in here. A nar-

row fissure on the right (south) has been dug out for about 20 m but has run in since. The alleged shaft in the floor depicted by Lloyd has never been seen in modern times.

A climb of 24 m up the eastern wall leads into Millers Chamber at a high level. A further climb of 12 m reaches Damocles Rift. Both these high chambers are decorated with numerous stalactites. The roof of Damocles Rift is only about 20 m below the surface.

A dye test using water released in the Main Chamber proved that the drainage went to Speedwell Cavern and thence to Russet Well.

Although Eldon Hole is developed along a group of parallel NNW-SSE fissures, little has been published concerning phreatic or vadose features but the dye test shows that any percolation water finds its way into the Perryfoot to Castleton drainage system.

16b THISTLE POT

Lying in the shallow dry valley branching north off the head of Conies Dale, this water-worn shaft has been dug out to a depth of 14 m. At the bottom a further drop of 3 m leads to

a short passage (24 m) and to a flooded bedding plane.

Nearby there are several choked fissures near the head of Conies Dale. Disused spar workings at Portway Mine have much clay fill derived from the

surrounding loess and may conceal a clay-filled pot. To the east, close to Hazard Mine, the loess sheet has several shallow dry valleys leading to a depression on Wham Rake which may well conceal a vein cavity.

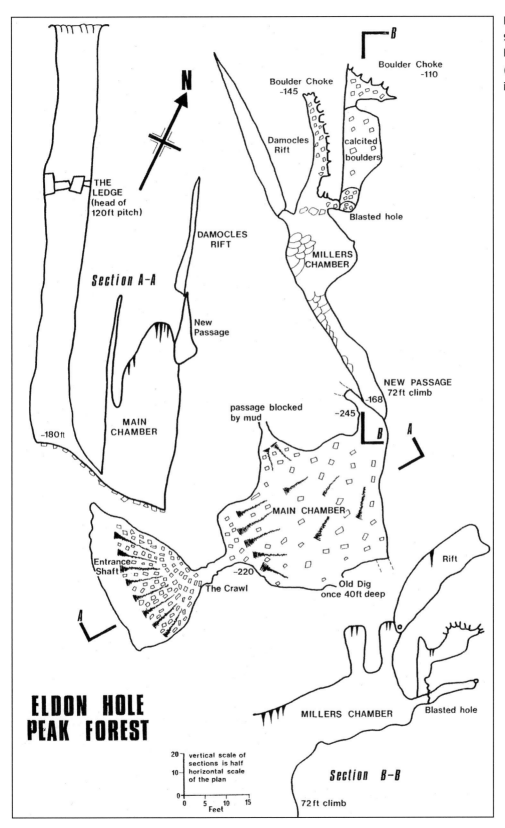

Plan and section of Eldon Hole (with depth in feet)

THE LEDGE (head of 120ft pitch)

DAMOCLES RIFT

Section A-A

New Passage

MAIN CHAMBER

-180ft

Boulder Choke -145

Damocles Rift

Boulder Choke -110

calcited boulders

Blasted hole

MILLERS CHAMBER

NEW PASSAGE 72ft climb

-168

-245

passage blocked by mud

B

A

MAIN CHAMBER

Rift

Entrance Shaft

-220

The Crawl

Old Dig once 40ft deep

A

ELDON HOLE PEAK FOREST

MILLERS CHAMBER

Blasted hole

20 — vertical scale of sections is half horizontal scale of the plan
10 —
0 —
0   5   10   15
Feet

Section B-B

72ft climb

17 OXLOW CAVERNS

The deep series of natural caverns in Faucet (Foreside) Rake (also known as Horsestones Rake in the Peak Forest Mining Liberty) was discovered by lead miners at an unknown date, probably in the early 18th century. They were later forgotten but in the late 19th century there was an abortive attempt to turn Oxlow Caverns into a show cave and the rotten miner's wooden stemples were replaced. However, climbing these did not appeal to visitors and the caverns were quietly forgotten again until an old miner drew the entrance shaft to the attention of the early 20th century cave explorers from Sheffield, W. Sissons and J. W. Puttrell.

Across the fields southwest of Oxlow House Farm the typical miners' shaft is 20 m deep and the system below was apparently once known as either Rickety or Rackety Mine and sometimes as Opens Mine, signifying that the miners were well aware of the presence of natural caverns. The shaft leads into the top of the First Cavern, with a very steep boulder slope leading west. Originally supported by miners' timbers, these became so rotten that some steel shuttering had to be installed. At the foot of the slope a short low passage doubles back to the head of the Second Pitch (11 m) into the Second Cavern, which opens into the vast East Chamber within a few metres. The Third Pitch (14 m) is down a slot in the wall of the East Chamber and lands the explorer on a col between the latter and a westward slope. A scramble down eastwards and

a drop of a few metres takes one to the floor of the East Chamber, more than 55 m high and 10 m wide; a miners' shaft sunk in its floor is largely obscured today. The miners climbed the east wall by wooden stemples across the mineral vein, and drove a short (9 m) blind level to the east, but no way on can be found. Taking the slope westwards from the col beneath the Third Pitch, West Swirl Passage is a steep scramble leading to a corkscrew down a short miners' by-pass shaft on to a platform below which is a steep slope to an overhanging drop. Slope and drop constitute the Fourth Pitch which totals 24 m (12 m slope and 12m overhang), leading into the West Antechamber. High on the right is the entrance to a complex of crawlways, including Pilgrims's Way and New Oxlow Series, which link Oxlow Caverns with Giants Hole: the access is via a pull-through rope system 9 m high.

At the foot of the Antechamber a low tube passage 35 m long brings a stream in from the north, with a sump 43 m long at the end; the stream sinks among boulders and is not seen again until it rises in Speedwell Cavern. Ducking under a low roof for a few metres the explorer enters the huge West Chamber, some 60 m long and of similar height. Miners' waste litters the floor. At the far end a miners' passage leads into the Far West Chamber, with a short shaft (5th pitch, 14 m) into Pearl Chamber where cave pearls have been deposited by the heavy drips falling from Maskhill Mine. The 6th pitch of 4.5 m drops into Pool

Chamber where the way on is blocked with miners' rubble in a sump. Far West Chamber forms the bottom of the Maskhill Mine series of caverns.

With its six ladder pitches and steep slopes between them Oxlow Caverns totals some 1400 m in length and 145 m in depth, terminating at the water-table between Giants Hole's East Canal and Speedwell's Main Rising.

The presence of miners' waste on the floors of both East and West Chambers shows that the lead miners must have worked there for a substantial period but the lengths of the mineral vein visible at present are limited. Cavers have climbed into the roof and found evidence that showed that the miners had been up there with the aid of wooden stemples, but little remains of these. Some preliminary processing of ore apparently took place on the cavern floors. There are legends of convict labour but no documentary evidence has come to light and it seems unlikely in the context of lead mining practice.

Oxlow Caverns are thus a fine example of a series of vein cavities, resulting from phreatic enlargement of vugs in Faucet Rake. Apart from the tube inlet at the foot of the West Antechamber there is little evidence of vadose development.

Maskhill Mine is a complex of old lead mine workings and natural caverns entered by cavers in the 1950s from a mine shaft about 180 m west of the Oxlow shaft. It is a series of high but narrow vertical caverns lying almost one above the other and

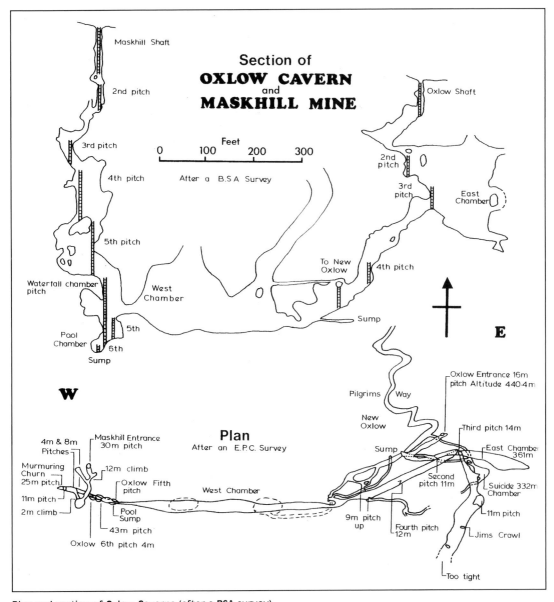

Plan and section of Oxlow Caverns (after a BSA survey).

reaching Oxlow's Far West Cavern at a depth of about 140 m. Parts of Maskhill Mine are well-decorated with flowstone; other parts have unstable boulder slopes. There are seven pitches of 30m, 15 m, 12 m, 26 m, 8 m, 43m and 4.5 m (the last is the 6th pitch in Oxlow Caverns).

Both Oxlow's and Maskhill's caverns are phreatic vein cavities developed by solution in Faucet Rake, the same vein that houses Speedwell's Bottomless Pit Cavern and several other caverns. The vein cavities were formed by phreatic solution at an early stage in the evolution of Castleton's cave systems. Apart from the low crawlway phreatic tube link passage to Giants Hole they seem to have been by-passed in later stream cave evolution. To-day, there is little sign of flooding and the drainage goes to Speedwell's Main Rising, about 1.5 km away.

A mine shaft east of Oxlow on Faucet Rake near the Rowter Farm track was explored in the 1940s. One man was lowered on a 30 m rope but landed on rotting sheep carcases which burst and the smell soon drove him out: he was kept at a discrete distance during the journey home.

18 NETTLE POT

Lying in an inconspicuous hollow on the moor about 150m southeast of Oxlow Cavern's shaft, Nettle Pot was found by W. Sissons in 1932. He named it after his dog Nettle. Removal of a few boulders revealed a narrow fissure with a NW-SE trend. Over the next two years several chokes were dug through by Sissons and other members of the Derbyshire Pennine Club. Digging sometimes required hanging head downwards and scooping out mud and rocks from below. Eventually the Narrows were cleared and the way was open down a bottle-shaped pothole oriented on a NW-SE fissure.

The entrance pothole is a natural shaft, not mined, and is 49 m deep. The Narrows are a section about 15 m down where the fissure is 3 m long but less than 30 cm wide making ladder-climbing awkward. Below the Narrows is the Sentry Box, an alcove large enough for two persons to rest, followed by the wider Bottle. At the bottom are the Flats, an extensive bedding cave formed in a much-weathered wayboard (a volcanic dust-clay) about a metre thick. The cave system extends both to northwest and southeast, but it is first necessary to descend into the Gulley chamber to one side via a 4 m pitch. The floor of the Gulley is composed of wedged rocks with a gaping hole into

Elizabeth Pitch, said to have been named in honour of the future Queen, then celebrating her birthday. It was first descended with the use of a wooden winch taken down the entrance shaft in pieces and assembled below. Before going into the deep Elizabeth Pitch and passing it with care the well-decorated Stalactite Passage extends northwest for 100 m to end in a grotto in an aven rising some 6 m, with a crawl going towards Oxlow Cavern's East Chamber at the top. Halfway along Stalactite Passage a hole in the floor goes down into Crumble Pot with Beza Pot below.

Returning to the Gulley and continuing southeast, a short climb down into Boulder Passage is followed by a climb back up into the Far Flats along the rotten wayboard, with a cavern below, Firbeck Hall. At the southeast end of the Far Flats a drop of 12 m takes one into Gour Passage and some 180 m further this ends in Derbyshire Hall.

The descent of Elizabeth is usually made via a small hole in the northwest corner of the Gulley, a pitch of 52 m alongside a mass of wedged blocks which look rather unstable. At the foot of the large chamber another pitch of 12 m reaches a small passage with a trickle of water entering from Firbeck Hall: a squeeze amongst boulders leads

to the bottom of Beza Pot.

Crumble Pot is 29 m deep and a short scramble then leads to Beza Pot, 46 m deep. Both Elizabeth and Crumble – Beza Pots are in the same fissure with masses of wedged boulders. Below Beza Pot a climb down amongst boulders in The Shakes leads to the final sump at a depth of 177 m. The Red River branch passage slopes upwards to the west into a fissure cavern parallel to the main joint.

Nettle Pot is unusual in the Castleton area in that it is on the intersection of a thick wayboard with a NW-SE joint with little sign of a mineral vein. Though no fault displacement has been detected, the wedged boulders suggest that there has been some fault movement. Otherwise the fissure shows only limited evidence of either phreatic or vadose development. Faulting on this trend suggests that there may be other similar un-mineralized fracture caves in the area but the only one found so far is **Mountbatten Pot**, some 400m to the south. This has been dug out to a depth of 42 m but becomes too tight for progress, though the bottom cannot be far above the wayboard in Nettle Pot's Flats. It is debatable whether this wayboard is at the same horizon as the Cave Dale Lava, but in view of its depth it seems unlikely.

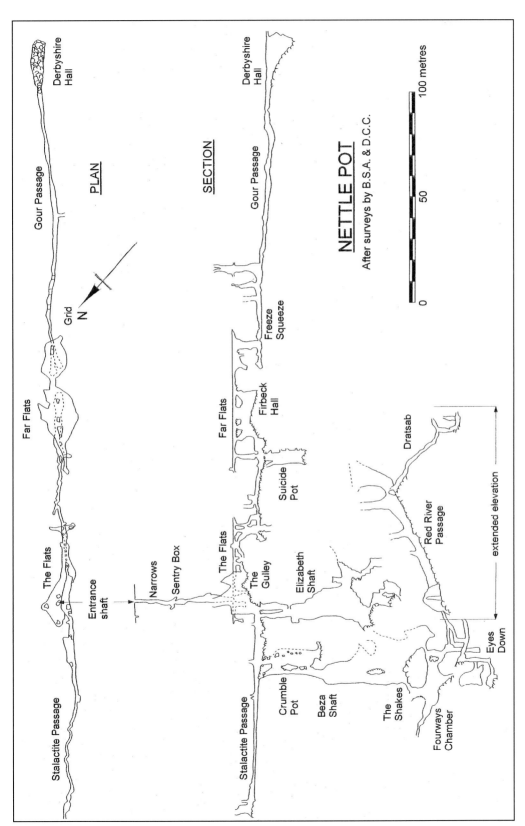

Section and plan of Nettle Pot. (from surveys by B.S.A. and D.C.C. Courtesy of John Beck).

19 LOST CAVERNS

Hollandtwine Mine was situated on Dirtlow Rake, some 30 m east of the gate on the rough road. The main haulage shaft was accessible until the 1970s but it has been obliterated by opencast workings for fluorspar and subsequent land restoration, so that neither the mine nor its cave are accessible today. The haulage shaft was 114 m deep with a partial bypass down a climbing way from 46 m depth. It was long ago recorded as having a "Great Swallow" at a depth of about 650 feet (200 m) roughly mid-way between Hollandtwine and Hazard Mines but this has not been seen in modern times and its nature is unknown. At about half the depth of the Great Swallow, a natural cave series was found to extend northeast from the 114 m haulage level. With some 340 m of low crawls there is a 21 m pitch midway where water sinks into a narrow fissure. A dye test showed that the water reappears at Ink Sump in Peak Cavern, confirming that the central part of Dirtlow Rake is in the Peak Cavern catchment. Diesel spillages in the fluorspar opencast workings are also reputed to have reached Peak Cavern.

Hurdlow Stile Pipe. (Hourdlo Steel Pipe). Our knowledge of this cave-cum-mine system is based on a late 18th century mine plan and section, which showed three shafts close to Hurdlow Barn apparently on either New Rake or the parallel Horsepit Rake. The shafts are about 20, 40 and 60 m deep and were joined at depth by what appears to be a cave passage sloping steeply to the east. The bottom of this cannot be far above the White River Series of Peak Cavern. There are several shafts in the area, all apparently collapsed or back-filled. Digging one out might reveal the "lost" cave but it has not been attempted so far.

Treak Cliff Back. Henry Watson of Ashford-in-the-Water was recorded in the lead miners' Barmaster's Book as having "16 pairs of stows on Treak Cliff Back for anything and what he could get" in 1765. Translated from miners' jargon, this refers to the flat top of Treak Cliff and that Watson was mining Blue John at 16 mines, each marked by a stows or wooden windlass. The positions and extent of these 16 mines is unknown and some were probably unroofed and changed beyond recognition by Czech refugees mining for fluorspar in the World War II period. However, it is still possible that there is a long-forgotten series of mines-cum-caves somewhere beneath the flat hilltop.

Old Tor Mine is not really a lost mine but it is often overlooked. It is in the northern slopes of the Winnats Pass and may have been one of Watson's sixteen mines: it was last worked by John Royse between the wars. Another old mine for Blue John was close to where the Winnats boundary wall meets the fence along the top of Treak Cliff, but the entrance shaft has been filled in for safety and its extent has not been recorded.

Remarks on Hoiurdlo Stile Plan

A is the West Forefield

B is the sump foot

C is the sump head

D is the west shaft foot: A-D is a shack with some lumps of ore

E is the Founder Shaft

F is the drift on the vein

G is the East Shaft foot

H is the sump head

J is the Swallow Drift mouth and the level of the spring

K is the forefield of the swallow

L is the mouth of the drift designed for the drawing gate

M is the second sump head

N is the sump foot

O is the Lodge and First Sump Foot

P is the east forefield of the Pipe

Right: Plan and section of Hurdlow Stile Pipe (after an undated c.1780 plan).

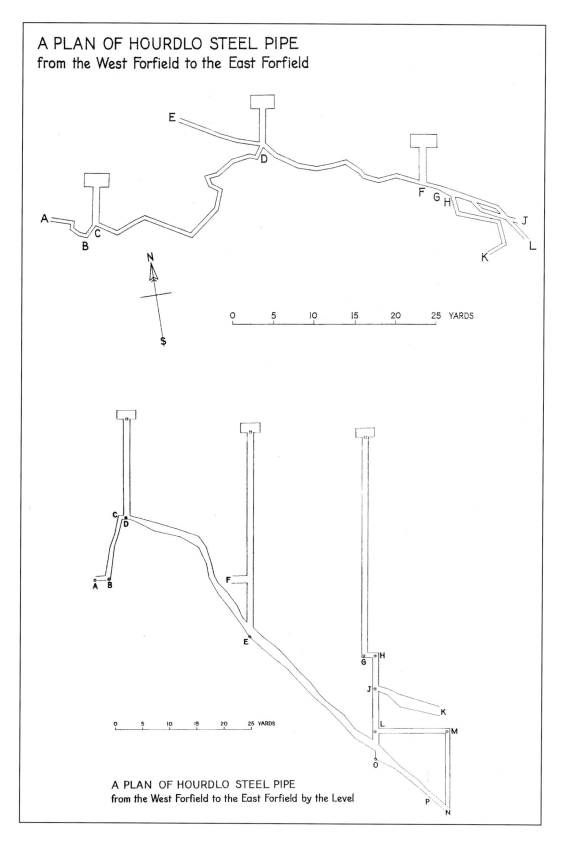

A PLAN OF HOURDLO STEEL PIPE
from the West Forfield to the East Forfield

A PLAN OF HOURDLO STEEL PIPE
from the West Forfield to the East Forfield by the Level

20 HYDROLOGY

The general pattern of the Castleton cave drainage system has been known since the late-18th-century lead-mining days when mining activities around Perryfoot caused turbid water to rise at Russet Well in Castleton.

There are two components of water input to the system: *autogenic* input from rain falling directly onto the limestone; and *allogenic* input from streams draining off the Millstone Grit on the southern slopes of Rushup Edge and flowing into swallets along the limestone/shale boundary. The autogenic input finds its way down from the limestone surface via joints, faults and mineral veins with diversions along toadstones and wayboards and enters the cave system as various inlets. The allogenic Millstone Grit catchment is about 5 square kilometres on the southern slopes of Rushup Edge and Mam Tor, and the autogenic catchment on the limestone is about 8.5 square kilometres, though its southern boundary is uncertain. The two types of input are chemically different, limestone water being only mildly acidic with an excess of calcium, whilst Millstone Grit water has little calcium and is more acidic and hence aggressive. The latter water is corrosive towards limestone and was responsible both for dissolving out phreatic caves and for enlarging vadose canyons. The percolation water from the limestone catchment leads to speleothem deposition in the vadose zone.

Water-tracing by dyes and chemical means dates only from the 1950s, though there are said to have been some early tests using salt which proved that the Rushup Edge swallets drained to Russet Well; details are unknown. In the early 20th century dye thrown into Speedwell Cavern's Bottomless Pit is alleged to have re-appeared at Russet Well 23 hours later. As the lake in the Bottomless Pit is some 12m higher than Russet Well there must be a free-running stream passage between them, though it has not yet been located. Dye tests by the Derwent Valley Water Board in 1952 confirmed the Coalpithole Mine to Russet Well link.

In the late 1970s a series of tests by Noel Christopher, using the green dye fluorescein and several other dyestuffs, confirmed the pattern of flow from the swallets to the Main Rising of Speedwell Cavern and thence to Russet Well. In the late 1980s Professor John Gunn and his students conducted over fifty more tests using fluorescein, rhodamine, and optical brighteners. These tests refined detailed knowledge of links within the system where more than twenty sumps are known. The flow system has variations in discharge at different stages of run-off as flood waters can sometimes overflow using different routes.

Flow switching between Speedwell's Main and Whirlpool Risings, which are about 8m different in altitude, could be due to temporary blockage(s) in the feeder conduit to Main Rising after flood events, with a return to "normal" conditions later as the blockage settles. At the deepest point of Main Rising sediment can be blasted out from a low slot during floods but slumps back afterwards. Total blockage of the feed to Main Rising causes water to resurge from Whirlpool Rising, but in drought conditions little or nothing rises from the latter. The difference in altitude indicates that there is probably some open passage somewhere in the system.

The southern boundary of the underground catchment of the Castleton area separating it from the Bradwell catchment is effectively unknown. Generally assumed to be along or near Dirtlow Rake, it is now known that some of the drainage from the middle part of that mineral vein goes to Ink Sump in Peak Cavern, whilst the dyes were also traced to resurgences in Bradwell. New Venture Mine and Long Rake on Bradwell Moor south of Dirtlow both have small streams but they are thought to drain to Bradwell. Domestic rubbish tipped down shafts on the north-eastern section of Dirtlow Rake contributes to the sediment in the Styx Inlet Sump in Peak Cavern's Halfway House. Some drainage from Dirtlow Rake goes to Pindale Sough in Hope Valley below Pindale: no dye tests are known to have confirmed this. Thus the location of the Peak Cavern and Bradwell drainage divide is unknown. Dye-traces of the drainage of the Slack Hole doline at the top of Cavedale and from the Dirtlow spar pit diverge to both Peak Cavern and to Bradwell. Thus to the south of the Castleton area the catchments of the Peak–Speedwell system

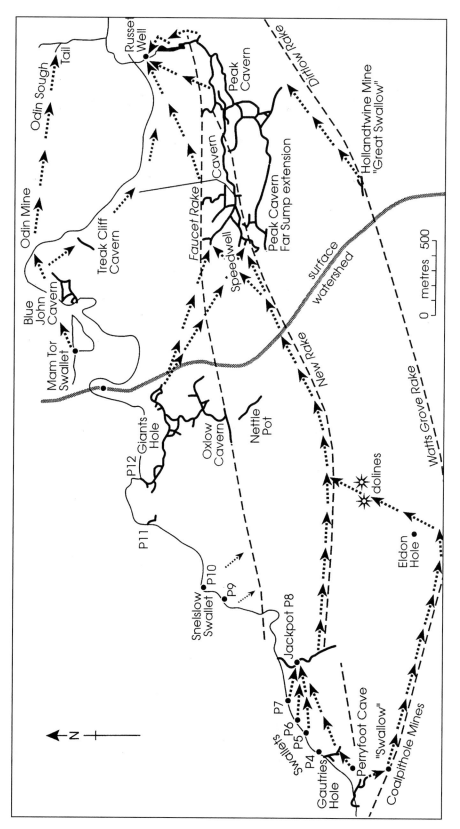

Sketch map of the underground drainage system of the Castleton area (by J. Gunn).

and the Bradwell resurgences appear to overlap. Pindale Sough and Cronstadt Sough under the cement works quarry have intermediate catchments but details are unknown. The western part of Dirtlow Rake and the veins extending westwards off it are probably on the Coalpithole to Russet Well drainage route but this has not been proven.

With a discharge point for Castleton's subterranean drainage at Russet Well at 187m O.D., a perennially flooded phreatic zone extends westwards beneath the lower part of the Peak–Speedwell cave system. Russet Well is in a poorly defined mineral vein, mainly calcite with some sphalerite. It has been dived to a depth of 25m and is probably to be described as a vein cavity; water enters from a slot too low for diving. The outlet for Speedwell's water must be very restricted to account for the back-up during floods. The Main Rising in Speedwell is at about 800ft O.D. (240m), close to if not identical with water levels in the East Canal of Giants Hole, in the bottom of Oxlow Caverns, Nettle Pot and the hidden sink in Coalpithole Mine, thereby demonstrating an almost flat water table at this altitude under the area from Speedwell Cavern to Perryfoot. The lost swallow in Hollandtwine Mine is perhaps 20 to 30m higher as it feeds Ink Sump in Peak Cavern; this hints at a southern boundary to the catchment near the middle part of Dirtlow Rake.

Peakshole Sough, which follows a vein under the western wall of Peak Cavern gorge, yields very little discharge today and has no obvious inlets at its west-

ern limit. Slop Moll is a spring outside the sough tail with a clear connection to Russet Well. Flood conditions give rise to a large spring in the field west of Goosehill Hall, but its source is unknown and any link to Slop Moll, to Peakshole Sough or the associated mine workings has not been demonstrated yet.

Amongst the findings of the dye tests are:

(1) The discharge from Speedwell Cavern reaches Russet Well by passing beneath the stream coming from Peak Cavern. Russet Well has been dived to a depth of 25m in a rather irregular mineral vein, possibly a vein cavity in the process of formation.

(2) Slop Moll, a spring arising outside Peakshole Sough, is directly connected to Russet Well, showing that there is effectively a U-tube beneath Peakshole Water stream. Most dye tests reaching Russet Well also affected Slop Moll. Russet Well and Slop Moll react to flood events in the same way, though they lie on opposite sides of the Peakshole Water stream.

(3) An injection of dye in water from a bowser into Eldon Hole took 1,100 hours to reach Russet Well, but injections into the dolines on the north-east flank of Eldon Hill only took 274 hours. Both went to Speedwell Cavern's Main Rising.

(4) Dyes placed in the small stream in Blue John Cavern appeared at Russet Well at periods ranging from 72 to 240 hours later, presumably after passing through the void system in the Boulder Bed along the foot of Treak Cliff and across the foot of the Winnats Pass.

(5) Dye injected into the Mam Tor Swallet stream went to Odin Sough, apparently distinct from any hydrological connection between Blue John Cavern and Russet Well, though Mam Tor Swallet has generally been assumed to be the source of the stream in the Blue John Cavern.

(6) There is a clear link between the Rushup Edge Swallets and Russet Well and Slop Moll, with the water mostly coming via Speedwell Cavern's Main Rising, but occasional flow switching means that the swallet water sometimes goes to Whirlpool Rising.

(7) Both Whirlpool and Main Risings exhibit ebbing and flowing characteristics according to preceding weather conditions, but with different periodicities. Whirlpool Rising occasionally ceases to flow in drought periods.

(8) The water last seen in Coalpithole Mine is thought not to follow that vein system until it meets Dirtlow Rake but to cross to the western extension of New Rake somewhere below Eldon Hill.

(9) A borehole in Eldon Hill quarry yielded water with a high salt content in winter, probably derived from de-icing road salt on Rushup Edge flowing into Jack Pot.

(10) Water from swallets P0 and P1 went to Coalpithole Mine, but the rest of the swallets drained to Jack Pot (P8), where it rose from a sump in a branch passage roughly aligned with New Rake.

(11) Water from Nettle Pot has been traced to both Main and Whirlpool Risings in Speedwell,

but water in Rowter Hole and Winnats Head Cave was only traced to Whirlpool Rising, suggesting that there is a division somewhere to the west of that Rising separating flows to either Main or Whirlpool Risings.

(12) Both Blue John Cavern's stream and Treak Cliff Cavern's limited drainage go to Russet Well but not via Speedwell. The drainage probably goes through the void system in the Boulder Bed at the foot of the reef slope.

(13) Normal flow in Peak Cavern's many inlets is autogenic percolation from the surrounding limestone plateau and from Dirtlow Rake. Flood conditions cause Speedwell's allogenic water to overflow into Peak Cavern via Treasury Sump, Speedwell Pot and Lumbago Walk, so that the discharge at Peak Cavern Resurgence is then a blend of au-togenic and allogenic water.

(14) Speedwell Cavern's stream is dominantly allogenic from the swallets but there are minor autogenic contributions from the inlets at the top of Cliff Cavern, and from the Bathing Pool sump.

Whilst the main subterranean drainage pattern is well established, there is a need for further tests at different seasons and at different stages of run-off such as snow-melt and heavy thunderstorms. The latter mean that flood events can occur at any season and Lumbago Walk in Peak Cavern can occasionally be submerged for periods varying from a few hours to a day or so. Similarly Speedwell Cavern's Bottomless Pit may fill to the level of the roof of the canal tunnels, but rarely for more than a few hours, almost always in winter.

It has been suggested that there may be a thermal element to the waters rising from deep flooded vein cavities, but no records of elevated temperatures are known.

It should be noted that any form of pollutant, such as sewage sludge fertilizer spread on fields as well as chemical or diesel spills, on any part of the catchment is liable to pass through the Castleton cave system and may affect the tourist caves as well as appearing at Russet Well. In the past both the Well and the Peakshole stream through the village have been contaminated for short periods. At one time Russet Well was an important village water supply, being pumped into the local mains before a regular supply from Ladybower Dam reached the village.

21 SPELEOGENESIS – THE EVOLUTION OF A CAVE SYSTEM

The origin and evolution of cave systems can be divided into two phases: firstly inception, covering the exploitation of any porosity or other pathways for water to move slowly through a limestone mass; and, secondly, development, when the initial pathways are enlarged enough to permit rapid turbulent flow and so to form caves. Inception may take many millions of years of geological time, whilst development covers a much shorter time, generally less than the last million years. Caves form by two main processes: solution and corrasion. Any acid can attack limestone and both carbonic acid, in rainwater or derived from soil, and sulphuric acid, from oxidizing pyrite in shale, are available. Corrasion is the mechanical attack by abrasive sediment washed through any voids formed by acid attack. The combination of solution accompanied by abrasion by inwashed sediment is a much faster process, resulting in the vadose canyons seen today. Both solution and abrasion can occur in totally submerged, phreatic conditions, or in open caves above the water table where they affect the floor and lower walls. The development of caves can also be summarized as a series of phases, starting with phreatic conditions in the fully saturated zone, and later vadose conditions when erosional features are developed above the water table. As adjacent valleys are deepened, so caves can be drained sufficiently to pass from phreatic into vadose conditions.

There is considerable chronological overlap in that some parts of a cave system may still be in the inception phase whilst others are well developed.

Phase 1: Inception. Once a mass of lime sediments is turned to stone and forms limestone it may retain pore spaces for the movement of water. However, the Carboniferous Limestone of the Peak District has very low porosity and such movement is negligible. Instead, water can exploit any weaknesses such as the breaks in sedimentation seen as bedding planes or the fractures caused by earth movements. Some bedding planes contain a few millimetres of pyritic shale so they are liable to yield a little dilute sulphuric acid and this can attack the bounding limestones. This is a slow process, but at least some effects were present by mid-Carboniferous times when both erosion and fracturing by earth movements led to ancient caves being available for later mineral infilling. Later in the Carboniferous period, in late Coal Measures times, further earth movements rejuvenated the fractures and hydrothermal fluids passed through them for several million years, at first opening them by dissolution of the limestone wall rock, and then precipitating minerals en route. The fractures became mineral veins, sometimes with gaps left between the mineral crystal layers as they grew inwards from opposing walls.

The mineralizing process took place when the limestones were buried under some 2km of Millstone Grit and Coal Measures, at temperatures of somewhat over 100°C, well insulated from whatever was happening on the surface of the deltas and coal swamps. So both the inception and the initial stages of development of bedding plane caves and at least the start of phreatic enlargement of vein cavities can be attributed to late Carboniferous times.

For about 300 million years, little happened in the deeply buried limestone, and any contained water was almost static. However, intermittent Earth movements, particularly in Cenozoic times (the last 65 million years), arched up the Pennine range, and tilted the Castleton area gently to the east by about 5 degrees. Some of the old fractures were re-opened and new ones were formed so that there are some fractures with mineral veins and some without. Removal of the cover strata by erosion set in during this long period, intermittently from Triassic times onwards, i.e. since around 200 million years ago. Although it is unknown what other strata replaced the cover of Millstone Grit and Coal Measures, it is likely that at least a kilometre of Jurassic and Cretaceous strata once covered the South Pennines. However, these were eroded off in early Cenozoic times and as a result of continued uplift and erosion, the limestone mass was progressively exhumed from mid-Cenozoic times onwards, say around 10 to 15 million years ago.

Phase 2: Unroofing of the limestone. As soon as at least a small patch of limestone was uncovered by erosion of the cover strata there was an opportunity for rainwater to sink into any available fracture system and to circulate within the limestone. Being slightly acidic with dissolved carbon dioxide and boosted by soil gases, it attacked the limestone. If an area of limestone say one kilometre across is visualized as being exposed across the highest parts of the plateau with its gentle easterly tilt, it would be possible for water to sink in the higher parts and to circulate through both bedding planes and mineral veins, only to rise again further downslope. Indeed with the limestone being effectively non-porous, water movement would concentrate in bedding planes and fractures. Shale partings in the bedding planes have limited permeability, but with pyrite oxidizing to sulphuric acid, transmission of water could slowly increase. Bedding planes with or without pyrite could also be opened slightly by stress release as unloading by removal of overlying strata occurs, admitting still more rainwater. Such solutional erosion occurred when the limestone mass, including fractures, was largely still within the phreatic zone. Phreatic solution is not limited to near surface action; it can be by waters circulating to great depths, perhaps as much as a kilometre. Solution is generally slow and both bedding planes and vein cavities were enlarged in parallel with further erosion of the Millstone Grit cover, in effect

the stripping back of the sheet of sandstones and shales, slowly enlarging the area of exposed limestone.

Phase 3: Vein cavities. Overlapping with phase 2, for millions of years before extensive unroofing, very slow circulation of groundwaters not only enlarged bedding planes but also initiated more cavities in the fractures. By late Pliocene times, say two million years ago, Castleton's karst was ripe for the stage of speleogenesis termed development, when percolating rainwater circulated more freely. Thus a complex system of shallow to deep circulation of rainwater utilized both bedding planes and the initial vein cavities, some probably inherited from mid-Carboniferous times, gradually enlarging the latter to produce such caverns as the Bottomless Pit, Oxlow Caverns, Leviathan and Titan. In some cases water probably rose from caves some far below even the present water table. Most vein cavities known today do not reach the surface as their inception was along mineral veins which were tight at high levels or which did not develop until water levels had started to fall. Eldon Hole and Nettle Pot were non-mineralized fractures widened at this stage. The Hope and Rushup Valleys were then probably no more than shallow channels across the Millstone Grit, with floors high above their present altitude.

Phase 4: Swallet Caves. The development of swallets taking water running off the early much larger versions of Mam Tor and Rushup Edge was mostly in the Quaternary Era, the last 1.8 million years. This era includes the Pleistocene Ice Ages, within which

there were several climatic oscillations with glaciations separated by warmer interglacial episodes. The recognition and dating of the full sequence and duration of these climatic changes is still a somewhat controversial matter for geologists. So far as the Peak District is concerned the only full glaciation recognized is the Anglian phase, named for its extensive deposits in East Anglia: ice probably more than a kilometre thick covered the whole limestone massif, but being sheltered by the Kinder Scout massif from the main glaciers streaming southwards on either side of the Pennines, the ice cap was less erosive and the Peak District has no corries or U-shaped valleys. The preceding Cromerian and earlier phases may have had glaciers across the Peak District but the evidence of these early glaciations is mostly confined to East Anglia. In the Castleton area cave sediments characteristic of the outwash from an early glaciation have been found in the Eldon Quarry fissures: they have been dated by palaeomagnetic methods to more than 780,000 years BP, perhaps as much as 900,000 years BP.

The Anglian glaciation was followed by the Hoxnian warm stage, and in turn by the Wolstonian cold phase, wherein it is doubtful whether there were glaciers in the South Pennines. The Wolstonian cold phase was followed by the Ipswichian warm interglacial, represented by a few uranium series dates on flowstone. The last glacial episode was the Devensian cold period, named from the Roman city of Deva (Chester); glaciers did not extend as far south as in the Anglian phase and just reached the Chapel-en-le-Frith area a few kilometres west of Castleton, so the White Peak experienced periglacial tundra conditions. There was a brief warm phase in mid-Devensian times, known as an interstadial. Cold but non-glacial phases were marked by a tundra climate with seasonal freeze and thaw alternations, resulting in the solifluction sheet descending from Rushup Edge.

The oscillations of climate with consequent changes in weathering, soil formation, vegetation cover, rainfall, run-off, snowfall and erosion, yielded a sequence of geomorphological changes to the White Peak landscape, though the full details are still uncertain. In particular, the oscillation saw the progressive deepening by incision of the rivers of the main Derbyshire Dales, mostly draining into the River Derwent. The Hope and Rushup valleys were gradually deepened. Dating the sequence of events shown by the development of the cave systems and correlating it with the major climatic changes and glacial advances is uncertain and speculative. There are few fossils to help in the traditional methods of dating the cave deposits. In recent decades dating stalagmites by their ^{238}uranium/^{234}thorium ratio has provided a partial framework, though the method can only be applied to speleothems which have grown in air-filled caves. Only a handful of dates have been determined for the Castleton area, so the rest of the sequence of events awaits further analyses.

In early to mid-Pleistocene times (i.e. pre-Anglian) early swallet cave development was down bedding planes (notably those with shale partings) to form a network of small phreatic tubes carrying water towards the vein cavities. The earliest swallets were probably well to the south of the present line in Rushup Valley, with relics seen in the Eldon quarry fissures and Sidetrack Cave. Windy Knoll Cave was probably a very early swallet but it has lost its catchment to the later erosion of Rushup Valley on one side and Hope Valley on the other. The structure of the lenticular (lens-shaped) reef mounds with undulating bedding planes along the limestone margin leads to markedly irregular up-and-down profiles as seen in the entrance series of Giants Hole and in the complex passages of the Perryfoot caves and Jack Pot.

As time progressed the upper parts of the phreatic tube network were drained and canyons began to be eroded in their floors both by dissolution and by the abrasive effects of inwashed

---

FOOTNOTE 1: Dating the glacials and interglacials is uncertain and subject to revision from time to time. The current estimates have been determined by different methods and should be regarded as a guide only. Dates are expressed as B.P. (Before Present, i.e. before 1950):

Holocene (post-glacial) the last 13000 years

Devensian (glacial) 116 000 – 13 000 years BP (with an interstadial 60 000-20 000 years BP)

Ipswichian (interglacial) 128 000-116 000 years BP

Wolstonian (cold) 200 000-128 000 years BP.

Hoxnian (warm) 380 000-200 000 years B.P.

Anglian (glacial) 460 000-380 000 years BP

Cromerian (various) before 460 000 years BP

Pre-Cromerian (several warm and cold phases) back to more than 1 million years BP.

Beginning of Quaternary 1.8 million years BP.

FOOTNOTE 2. Uranium series dating depends on a small amount of uranium, a few parts per million, being extracted from the limestone above the caves and redeposited with calcite in stalagmites where radio-active decay takes place at a known rate. If the ratios of the isotopes 238uranium and 234thorium are measured the results are indications of the duration of radio-active decay. The method has a limit of about 350 000 years as too little uranium is left for measurement beyond that date.

Dates obtained from Castleton stalagmites – in 1000s of years B.P. (Ford, Gascoyne & Beck, 1983):

Treak Cliff Cavern 125 ± 6 and 121 ± 4

Winnats Head Cave (upper series) 186 ± 7 and 191 ± 15

Speedwell Cavern (Bung Hole Series) 96 ± 4

Peak Cavern (fallen block) 59 ±3, 51 ±2 and 73 ± 2

Giants Hole 3.4 ± 0.1, 17 ± 2, 54 ± 2, 48 ± 1, 125± 2, 3.6 ± 2 and 2.2 ± 2

sand. To the south of the reef belt, the swallet streams entered more regularly bedded lagoonal limestones and eroded the upper parts of the vadose canyons such as the narrow Crabwalk in Giants Hole. Hope Valley was still shallow and much of the limestone mass was still submerged, i.e. in the phreatic zone below the water table (roughly the level of the resurgences then active). The streams flowing into the swallets had to resurge somewhere and the origin of Peak Cavern's gorge and entrance can be ascribed to a Vauclusian spring (named after the deep-seated spring of Fontaine de Vaucluse in the south of France) discharging onto a Hope Valley floor much higher than at present. Peak Cavern was still submerged in the phreatic zone as water overflowed via a lip at a high point in the gorge, gradually eroded away later.

Phase 5: Lowering the water table. As Castleton lay in the protective shadow of Kinder Scout and the rest of the Pennines, the Anglian glaciers were at best mildly effective around Castleton, and neither erosional forms such as corries and U-shaped valleys nor depositional forms such as boulder clay or moraines were formed there. With the gradual lowering of valley floors by river erosion, the water table fell and the cave systems were gradually drained and vadose canyons were eroded into the floors of phreatic tubes. Run-off would be enhanced by seasonal snow-melt during the periglacial conditions of the cold Wolstonian and Devensian phases and water cascading through caves would carry much abrasive sediment. With little vegetation or soil, dry valleys (i.e. valleys

without streams today) were incised into the frozen ground: hence Cavedale, Perry Dale, Conies Dale and the Winnats Pass (though the latter was initiated as a mid-Carboniferous inter-reef channel partly filled by shale in Millstone Grit times). The limestone was progressively uncovered, the limestone-shale boundary retreated northwards towards its present position, and the present swallet caves were developed. At first they were no more than phreatic tubes with streams along the floors, but with input from streams draining the sandstones and the solifluction sheet of Rushup Edge bringing abrasive sand, their vadose canyons were progressively deepened.

Although only a few remnants have been found so far, it seems likely that there may have been a high-level vadose cave system, possibly represented by such caves as Sidetrack and the White River Series of Peak Cavern. Perhaps there is an as yet undiscovered cave system linking the two? Another early swallet was on the face of Treak Cliff: fed by a stream flowing off a larger version of Mam Tor, this cavern has a phreatic tube in the roof and grottoes in a vadose canyon. Uranium series dates from stalagmites are about 125,000 to 131,000 years, in the Ipswichian interglacial. Another stream draining Mam Tor carried much run-off into the Blue John Cavern, eroding its vadose canyon. Both of these exploited former mineralized palaeokarstic caverns that have partial mineral linings in and below the mid-Carboniferous Boulder Bed.

Phase 6: Continued meltwater erosion. In the Wolstonian cold phase, the lack of a vegeta-

tion cover and continued solifluction yielded run-off water with abrasive sand and the canyon passages were deepened still more. It was followed by the Devensian cold phase when the wind-blown dust known as loess blanketed the Peak District, but with a brief warm mid-Devensian interstadial allowing stalagmite growth around 51,000 to 59,000 years BP. Washed into caves, some of the loess was redeposited as the sticky yellowish mud for which Derbyshire caves are well known among cavers. Earlier sheets of loess may have been present but they have not been distinguished. Similarly the dry valleys may have their origin in multiple periods of incision by run-off across frozen ground from Anglian times onwards.

Phase 7: Post-glacial: continued entrenchment and stalactite growth. Run-off of rainwater during both the Devensian and post-glacial times (Holocene – the last 13,000 years) brought more deepening of vadose canyons by abrasive sediment. Most stalactites and stalagmites visible today have grown in the warmer post-glacial Holocene period, but a few have their origins in the Ipswichian interglacial and in the mid-Devensian interstadial. Stalagmites have grown on top of inwashed loessic mud in Treak Cliff Cavern. Little stalactite growth was likely during the permafrost conditions of either Wolstonian or Devensian times when the frozen ground allowed little or no percolation water to enter the caves. The streams draining Rushup Edge caused incision of channels cut into the solifluction sheet. The continued deepening of Hope Valley permitted the

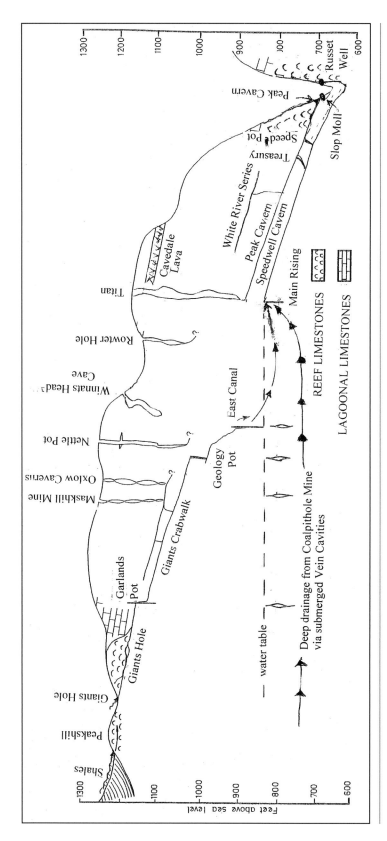

Peak Cavern Gorge's lip to be eroded away with the resultant loss of the Vauclusian spring and partial draining of Peak Cavern. Both the lower parts of the Peak and Speedwell Caverns are vadose streamways running down drained phreatic tubes into flooded sections where phreatic processes are still active. The erosion of the floor of Peak Cavern gorge exposed a mineral vein at Russet Well and much of the cave drainage now rises via a submerged vein cavity system.

The lowest 15m or so of the main Peak and Speedwell streamways are drained phreatic tubes where very little no incision has taken place as yet. The floor of the vadose canyons just above this height (195m) corresponds with the only river terrace recognizable in the Hope Valley. So, unfortunately it is not yet possible to correlate earlier events in the evolution of the cave systems with parallel events in the erosion of Hope Valley.

Thus Castleton's cave systems have a complex profile today comprising alternations between vadose and phreatic conditions, effectively vadose–phreatic–vadose–phreatic. Many drained vein cavities and bedding plane tubes are now in the vadose zone but some still channel water into caves in the phreatic zone. Vadose canyons have developed in the swallets draining into the vein cavity systems, rising again into tubes where the floors have been eroded into the massive canyons

Diagrammatic section from Giants Hole to Russet Well to show the relationship of mineral veins and cavities to bedding-controlled stream caves.

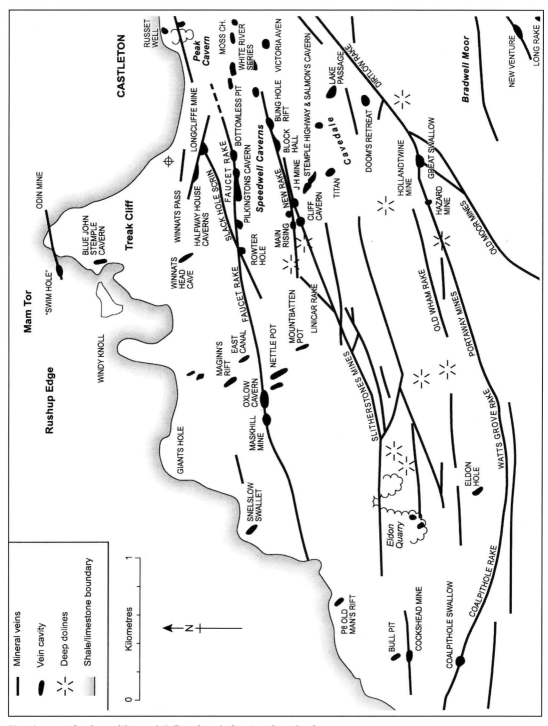

Sketch map of vein cavities and dolines in relation to mineral veins.

in Speedwell and Peak Caverns (and Blue John Cavern with its misfit stream). The uranium series dates show that most of the high-level caves had been drained by Ipswichian times and were available for stalagmite growth.

The evolutionary process still continues with enlargement of as yet inaccessible vein cavities below the water table, with deepening of the stream canyons,

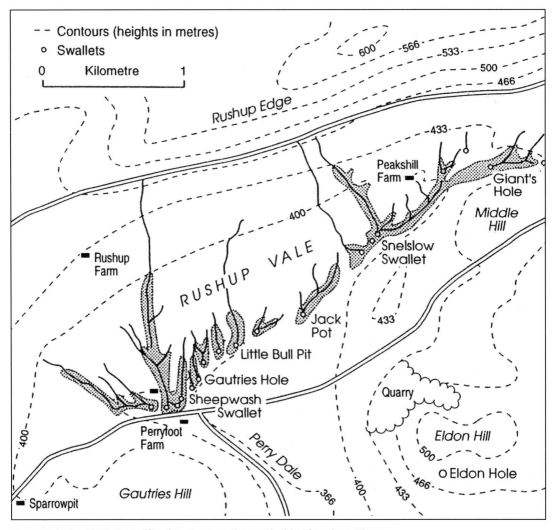

Channels incised into the solifluction sheet on the south side of Rushup Edge.

and continued stalactitic growth. With an average 230 parts per million of calcium carbonate removed in the water rising from Russet Well, more limestone is being taken away in solution in a year than the quarries usually extract. Many thousands of years into the future, when Hope Valley is deepened still further, the lower ends of the Speedwell and Peak streamways will open out into vadose streamways flowing out onto a Hope Valley floor at a lower altitude than at present.

The Windy Knoll ridge forms an apparent surface divide, but the cave systems take water from the swallets on the west eastwards to the main caves east of the ridge; otherwise the Rushup Vale would form part of the Wye Valley catchment, distinct from Hope Valley's. During at least one frozen ground phase the run-off from Rushup Valley flowed down the now dry valley of Perry Dale and thence to the River Wye.

This speleogenetic sequence departs from the theoretical normal pattern in having the additional complications of the marginal reef limestones, scattered sheets of lava and clay-wayboards, the mid-Carboniferous Boulder Bed and associated ancient karst features (palaeokarst), and the mineral veins with their vein cavities. Without the continuing deepening of Hope Valley the limestone mass would still be waterlogged in the phreatic zone. Over the last million years or so erosion has lowered the water table and many of the caves we know today were largely developed by the growth of vadose canyons.

The latter part of the 20th century saw great advances in cave exploration: who would have forecast the vast Titan Cavern before its discovery a few years back? There is still a large gap between the swallets and where the water re-appears in Speedwell Cavern's Main Rising. Digging out sediment-filled passages heading west from both Speedwell and Peak Caverns has so far made only limited advances into the unknown. Similarly, diving in sumps heading westwards seems to have reached the limits of being penetrable. So where should cavers try next?

There is little doubt that digging will bring results in due course – but where? Sinking shafts into the dolines on the plateau may well involve engineering projects lasting several years. Bull Pit has been tried without success. Removing the accumulation of rocks thrown down Eldon Hole would require a crane and bucket for weeks if not months, as well as a lot of labour – perhaps volunteers. Another possibility would be to sink a shaft at the point where shallow channels in the loess sheet converge on Wham Rake a hundred metres or so west of Hazard Mine.

Digging underground could be more profitable. Following the stream course in Little Bull Pit might necessitate clearing the pothole above but could

open up a new stream cave. Could Sidetrack Cave in Eldon Quarry be extended? It is worth considering the fissures full of sands and clays in the same quarry, but clearing any of them might take years. The mud-filled passages above Squaw's Junction in Peak Cavern have been partly cleared but it would be a long job to follow what appears to be a "fossil" stream course above and to one side of the main streamway. Similarly, digging out choked passages near Cliff Cavern in Speedwell could take a long time. Breaking through the stalagmite-cemented boulder blockage at the western end of the White River Series could lead to an extension of that "fossil" high-level stream cave. Similarly, the eastern downstream end might lead into another part of that ancient streamway. In Speedwell Cavern, clearing the broken rock chippings (miners' waste?) from the holes in the roof above Whirlpool Passage might yield access to the Nether Pipe. Digging out the rubble in the back of Windy Knoll Cave has been tried but caused a subsidence on the surface: another try elsewhere might be more fruitful.

Diving has reached its limits in many sumps but there are still a few worthy of further exploration. The Styx Inlet Sump in Peak Cavern's Halfway House was only found in 2005 but a

diver has penetrated 100m to reach a blockage; underwater digging may penetrate this. In Far Peak Extension the Rasp and adjacent Flatmate might yield to digging. Major Sump in Far Peak Extension is an enigma – it has obviously discharged a large stream in the past, but is now blocked; would underwater digging be possible?

Concentrated effort in some of the old lead mines might bring results. The old miners often entered natural caverns but left little or no record as they were not interested in them except for disposal of their waste rock or draining off water. Although Oxlow Caverns were known under their alternative name of "The Opens", they had been forgotten until brought to Puttrell's attention. The nearby Maskhill Mine and Rowter Hole were not recorded as caverns. There may be other caverns in old lead mines as yet undiscovered. Could the lost Hurdlow Stile Mine be re-opened by testing the shafts around Hurdlow Barn? Could the mid-depth caverns or the alleged swallow at the bottom of Hollandtwine Mine be re-entered by digging out the shaft?

These are just a few thoughts which might bring results. Others will doubtless have other ideas and I look forward to hearing about any discoveries one day.

FURTHER READING

There is a wealth of literature on the Castleton caves, much of it in caving club journals with limited availability. A selection is given below. Most items should be obtainable via public lending library services.

Christopher, N.S.J., Crabtree, R.W. & Culshaw, S.M. 1981. A hydrological study of the Castleton area. *Transactions of the British Cave Research Association*, vol. 8, pp. 186–206.

Cordingley, J.N. 1986. *The Peak Cavern System – A Cavers Guide.* Vitagraph Books, Manchester. 64 pp.

Cordingley, J.N. 2000. Vein cavities in the Castleton caves: further information. *Cave & Karst Science*, vol. 27, no. 2, pp. 85–88.

Ford, T.D. 1977. *Limestones and Caves of the Peak District.* Geo-Books, Norwich. 469 pp.

Ford, T.D. 1986. The Evolution of the Castleton Cave Systems and related features. *Mercian Geologist*, vol. 10, no. 2, pp.91–114.

Ford, T.D. 1991. Speleogenesis – the evolution of the Castleton caves. *Geology Today*, vol. 12, no. 3, pp. 101–109.

Ford, T.D. 2000. Vein cavities: the early evolution of the Castleton cave systems. *Cave & Karst Science*, vol. 27, no. 1, pp. 5–14.

Ford, T.D. 2003. *Rocks and Scenery of the Peak District.* Landmark Publishing, Ashbourne. 96 pp.

Ford, T.D. 2005. *Derbyshire Blue John.* Landmark Publishing, Ashbourne. 2nd edition, 112 pp.

Ford, T.D., Gascoyne, M. & Beck, J.S. 1983. Speleothem Dates and Pleistocene Chronology in the Peak District of Derbyshire. *Cave Science*, vol. 10, no. 2, pp. 103–115.

Ford, T.D. & Gunn, J. 2008. *Karst and Caves of the Peak District.* British Cave Research Association: Cave Studies Series.

Ford, T.D. & Rieuwerts, J.H. 1999. *Lead Mining in the Peak.* Landmark Publishing, Ashbourne. 4th edition. 208 pp.

Gill, D.W. & Beck, J.S. 1991. *Caves of the Peak District.* Dalesman Publishing, Clapham, Lancaster. 257 pp.

Gunn, J. 1991. Water-tracing Experiments in the Castleton Karst, 1950–1990. *Cave Science*, vol. 18, pp. 43–46.

Heathcote, C. 2001. A history and gazetteer of the mines in the Liberty of Peak Forest, 1605–1878. *Mining History*, vol. 14, no.5, pp. 1–28.

Heathcote, C. 2008. A gazetteer of the lead mines with Castleton and Hope Liberties 1748-1898. *Mining History* Vol 16, pp1-30

Marsden, A.W. 1991. Aspects of the Peak–Speedwell Cave System. *Cave Science*, vol. 18, no. 1, pp. 3–18 (with several additional contributions pp.19–58).

Nash, D.A. & Beck, J.S. 1989. *A Peak Cavern Bibliography.* British Cave Research Association. 90 pp.

Nixon, D.A. & Warriner, D. 1997. The connection of James Hall Over Engine Mine to Peak and Speedwell Caverns. *Mining History*, vol. 13, no. 3, pp. 57–67.

Puttrell, J.W. 1937. The Bottomless Pit and Beyond. *Caves & Caving*, vol. 1, no. 2, pp. 44–47, and vol. 1, no. 3, pp. 85–88.

Puttrell, J.W. 1938. To the top of the Bottomless Pit. *Caves & Caving*, vol. 1, no. 4, pp. 125–126.

Quirk, D.G. 1985. The mineralogy and paragenesis of Speedwell Mine, Castleton. *Mercian Geologist*, vol. 10, pp. 39–60.

Quirk, D.G. 1986. Mineralization and stress history in North Derbyshire. *Bulletin of the Peak District Mines Historical Society*, vol. 9, no. 6, pp. 333–386.

Rieuwerts, J.H. 2007. *Lead Mining in Derbyshire: History, Development and Drainage. Vol. 1: Castleton to the Wye Valley.* Landmark Publishing, Ashbourne. 192 pp.

Rieuwerts, J.H. & Ford, T.D. 1985. The Mining History of the Speedwell Mine or Oakden Level, Castleton. *Bulletin of the Peak District Mines Historical Society*, vol. 9, no. 3, pp. 129–170.

Winder, F.A. 1938. *An Unconventional Guide to the Caverns of Castleton.* Hartley Seed, Sheffield. 81 pp.

Glossary

Adit: A tunnel excavated horizontally to provide access to a mine.

Aven: A term for a cavern rising vertically above a cave passage, originating in France.

Barmaster: An official appointed by the Crown or a lessee to supervise all legal matters concerning lead mining; required to keep a book of all transactions and ownership of lead mines.

BP: Before the present: an expression used for dates of sub-fossil materials; usually taken as before AD 1950.

Choke: A jumble of fallen rocks blocking a cave passage.

Doline: A funnel-shaped hollow on the surface of a limestone area signifying a focal point for solution; often associated with the collapse of a cave below.

Fault: A break in rocks where two masses have moved past each other, i.e. with displacement.

Fracture: A break in strata where no displacement can be detected.

Ginged: The upper part of a mineshaft where loose ground is supported by built walling.

Gour pool: A shallow pool on a stalagmite floor where slow-moving water deposits a rim – also known as rimstone pool.

Karst: A collective term for limestone landscapes and their distinctive features.

Loess: Wind-blown dust which has settled on the barren areas at the margins of an ice sheet.

O.D.: Above Ordnance Datum, i.e. above sea level.

Palaeokarst: An ancient (fossil) limestone landscape.

Periglacial: Around the margins of an ice sheet.

Phreatic: Refers to features developed by solution below the water table.

Rake: A major mineral vein, usually deposited in a fault.

Scrin: A minor mineral vein filling a subsidiary fracture, often branching from a larger fracture or rake.

Slickensides: Grooved, sometimes polished, surfaces where rock masses have slipped past each other during fault movements.

Solifluction: The sludging movement of surface deposits caused by alternating freeze and thaw processes.

Sough: A more or less horizontal tunnel excavated for drainage of nearby mines.

Speleothem: Any calcareous deposit such as a stalactite, stalagmite, helictite or flowstone.

Streamway: An underground stream course forming the principal part of a cave system.

Sump: A completely flooded part of a cave system.

Swallet: A cave which engulfs an inflowing stream (sometimes called a sinkhole or swallow hole).

Tail: The outfall point of water from a sough.

Turbid: Muddy, with suspended sediment carried by a stream in flood.

Vadose: The zone of a limestone mass above the water table, often with open stream passages; the features of erosion above the water table.

Vug: A cavity in a mineral vein, often lined with crystals.

Wayboard: A parting between limestone beds, usually containing a few centimetres of greenish clay, originally volcanic dust.